BEHIND THE SURGERY DOOR

Behind the
Surgery Door

Life as a Practice Nurse

L. Smart

Book Guild Publishing
Sussex, England

First published in Great Britain in 2010 by
The Book Guild Ltd
Pavilion View
19 New Road
Brighton, BN1 1UF

Typeset in Baskerville by Ellipsis Books Limited, Glasgow

Printed in Great Britain by CPI Antony Rowe

A catalogue record for this book is available from The British Library.

ISBN 978 1 84624 395 0

For Keith, Craig and the family

Contents

Author's Note

I trust that my memory has not failed me as I have endeavoured to recall happenings that I have experienced over the past 42 years of nursing. I have tried to be truthful about the tales and stories I heard from the patients in this book but, to protect their identity, I have changed their names, along with those of colleagues and places. I have tried to give a clear account of unchanged stretches of flowing incidents and flashes of humour which I have had the pleasure of sharing with the population I have worked with.

Acknowledgements

I am grateful to the surgery for keeping me employed in a job I loved and for allowing me to commit both my time and intellectual effort to attend courses over the years necessary for my professional development in order that I might progress as a practitioner. I would like to thank the practice population for making my job so enjoyable and for the tales and stories related to me when they attended for treatment. In addition I would like to thank the staff I have had the pleasure of working with and for making me laugh. Finally, I thank friends and family, who provided ongoing support and encouragement throughout the writing of this book.

Introduction

Few of us have been born with a silver spoon in our mouth. However, those of us who are meant to work our way through life in an attempt to reach our goal, whatever that goal might be, have a choice whether or not to make full use of the riches we have. Of course I don't see these as riches as in wealth, but I believe we all are capable of using our riches and that each one of us has riches within. How we decide to use them or not is up to us as we make our journey along the path in life.

As for me, this journey could only be enhanced by using one of the riches bestowed upon me which had to be my sense of humour, and since I freely received it I could only freely pass it on and try and draw out the humour there was in all I came in contact with, which included the many patients I nursed and cared for throughout my professional career. Although laughter does not cure illness or relieve pain, it does play a large part in removing some of the fears and anxieties that can afflict those unfortunate to become sick. Often it has been a means to help relax people, and at the same time has formed a bond by encouraging trust in one another.

Throughout the years, what I lacked in other forms of wealth was replaced by the knowledge that I was, more than most, surrounded by a family who shared the same sense of humour. This is yet another of the great riches I have been honoured to have: the love and protection which my family surrounded me with as I grew up, and which stayed with me when I left home and went out into the world at large, eventually leading me *Behind the Surgery*

Door. So it would be remiss of me not to introduce you to some of the members of my family and tell you about a few of the antics we got up to as I was growing up in Scotland.

1

The Runaways

It all began a long time ago in the Royal Burgh of Lanark, a historic town 25 miles from Glasgow and 33 miles from Edinburgh, situated in the rolling landscape of the Upper Ward of Lanarkshire overlooking the River Clyde. This was the home of the famous William Wallace, a Scottish hero who killed the English Sheriff of Lanark in May 1297 as he tried to win the country's freedom from English rule. Born on 2nd May 1945 I was the youngest of six, with two brothers and three sisters. My father, whose word was law in the Dickie household, was a hard-working, handsome family man with black curly hair. He washed it every morning and because it was still wet when he left the house it could be seen by all, glistening as the daylight caught the beads of water nestling in his curls on his way to work. Every Friday night he would come home with a pocket full of sweets and chocolate bought from his hard-earned wages, and after everyone had dinner he would share out the delights between us. Before doing so he would tease Richard (who is seven years older than me) and Helen (who is five years older), making them guess what pocket the sweets were in, and they would respond by chasing him about the house until they finally pinned him down and raided his pocket containing the delicious sweets – which did not last very long.

Apparently, he would then take me on his knee and feed me the chocolate while Helen would take up her position at his feet and having eaten her share would wait to catch any bits of chocolate I dropped. This was a game that came to an abrupt end because my father's death was sudden and unexpected; even the night before he died he was mending the school shoes and had not complained about feeling unwell. This was just four days before his forty-first birthday; I was almost eight months old so the knowledge I have of him has been collected from each member of the family.

My brother John, who is 16½ years older than me, recalls my father as a no-nonsense stern man; perhaps that was because as a teenager John needed to be taken in hand – he was just like most youngsters who are full of energy and seeking adventure. An example of this was the time that John decided to run away from home with his mates. It was a Sunday evening when John and three of his mates decided they had had enough of work and could not face the Monday morning so they took off to seek their fortune and headed for London with a total of 8 shillings between them.

Their first night was spent at Abington (16 miles from Lanark), where they slept in a barn, then each day would begin with them washing themselves in brooks or burns (how they dried themselves was another matter) before begging from door to door for a sandwich or a drink of water, they were depending entirely on the kindness of the folk they encountered. However, after four nights of sleeping rough they did manage to get as far as Stockport. This is where they saw an advertisement asking for workers at the Squirrel Sweet Factory near Manchester. Thinking their luck was in, the four ragamuffins approached the owner who took one look at the state they were in before chasing them from his door.

Having spent their last four pennies on a loaf of bread, they decided to give themselves up to the nearest police station, when the police were faced with these boys standing before them looking bedraggled, hungry and weary. They placed them in a cell where they were given a large mug of tea and a thick slice of bread and jam, which was gratefully received and soon devoured, while the police notified the families who had reported them missing from home. In order to send the wayward lads home the families were asked to pay for their train fare. However, the police told John that his dad was the only one who refused to send the fare. 'He got himself there, he can get himself back,' was my dad's reply.

My mother, unknown to my dad, went in desperation to my granny to ask her if she would pay the train fare; without hesitation Granny paid the fare, but she did insist that when John returned home he should come and stay with his granddad and her for a time, to allow my father to cool off. John was only too grateful to be back in his home town again, and to be able to keep clear of retribution for a bit, so there was no problem with him staying at his grandparents' for a short time – which turned out to be at least three months.

When the runaways got off the train at Carstairs they kissed the platform, saying, 'Scotland, we will never leave you again.'

John later did leave home after the death of my father when on 6th August 1946 he joined the Royal Navy – this also was an act of impulse, when he went with his mates to sign on, and to his shock he was the only one of them that passed his medical. So the impulsive act backfired on him when he was left to sail the seas alone without his old mates. Nevertheless, being a handsome chap in his younger days he was never alone for long: having the gift of the gab, John was a hit with the ladies. Until, that is, he met his Jean and knew she was the girl for him. Fearing that while he was away from home she might meet another, when John was overseas in the Navy he wrote a letter to Jean. The letter romanced about how her skin was like a peach. Of course it was just after the Second World War and food, let alone fruit, was still rationed and in short supply, so it was not surprising that Jean, who had never even seen a peach, ran to her mother in her excitement and asked her what a peach looked like. Her mother, preoccupied with something and not knowing why she was asking, replied, 'Oh! It is a yellow hairy thing.'

Such an uncomplimentary answer did not appear to deter Jean, who was a dark-haired, blue-eyed beauty, because later when John was demobbed and came home from the Navy they were married, and had two children.

I think it is fair to say that John's first love had to be his family, but following close behind was his love of football, and in his teens he had played for his local team, and knew how to kick a ball. Jean was not without her own talents, with her knowledge of the French language that she had been taught at school, but although she did not get the opportunity to travel to the Continent, at least not in her younger days with a young family (her daughter Cathleen, then later her son Ian), she would often in later years quote a variety of phrases to me just to keep her knowledge of the language fresh in her mind.

Travelling was the last thing John was wanting to do after his time away from Scotland. He was quite content to enjoy the company of his own folk in his native land, and of course his football, which he had missed while in the Navy.

I was only 15 months old when John left to join the Navy, and I was too young to remember him going. The earliest memory I have was of when I was about three, and I had been left sleeping on the couch in the living room while my mother had rushed to the shops. I remember waking to a quiet house and coming off the couch and trotting through the lobby to the kitchen, looking for my mammy and not finding her there, I climbed on a chair to look through the kitchen window, and not seeing a soul outside I started to bawl in panic at being alone.

Our home was a ground-floor flat in the corner of a cul-de-sac and the kitchen window looked up the cul-de-sac on to the road that led to the shops. I still have that vivid memory of that dull wet day and crying for my mammy; it was pouring with rain, probably the reason my mother decided not to wake me and take me out in it, thinking I was in a deep sleep and that she would get back home before I woke.

One of the neighbours who lived higher up the cul-de-sac saw me from her window and quickly came and carried me, hurrying in the rain, to her house. Once indoors she placed me on the rug in front of a cosy coal fire which had a large fireguard surrounding it, and here she gave me some toys to play with before she settled to watch by her window for my mother to return. When my mother did return she was all flustered and out of breath because she had been rushing up the hill from the shops, carrying her heavy shopping bag. The look of relief on her face was obvious as she entered the neighbour's house and picked me up. I was delighted to see her back, but reluctant to leave the new-found toys behind.

In those days neighbours looked out for each other with a real sense of community spirit; however, at the same time everyone knew everyone else's business and people were usually aware of each other's circumstances, good or bad, causing them to keep an eye on each other's children, and most of the neighbours would not hesitate to correct the children or tell them off if they thought it was needed in an attempt to help keep them out of trouble, with no fear of upsetting their parents in doing so.

Two years later, my first day at school conjures up memories of Mother taking me to my beginners' class which was held in a large wooden hut situated in a corner of the playground of Lanark Primary School. Once inside the wooden door I found myself in the cloakroom where I was shown by the teacher where to hang my coat. I was too busy undoing the many buttons on my coat, then trying to hang it on the big black hook, to notice my mother making her escape through the same door. Once my coat was neatly hung up I was then taken through a middle door in the cloakroom which led into the classroom and it was here, faced with a lot of children, that it dawned on me that my mother was missing. I instantly started to bawl, causing some of the other children to start crying because they could hear someone else was. The fraught teacher was left to deal with me and the other weeping children.

From then onwards things got better. I enjoyed school, especially at the end of the week when every Friday afternoon at the end of lessons (perhaps given as a bribe to get us to come back on Monday) we were each presented with a brown paper poke full of multicoloured sugared rice crispies, which I ate on the way home.

It was while I was still in the first class that I had my first injury, which seemed dramatic to me at the time. It happened one day when I was coming home from school with my sister Helen and some of her friends; while they were hanging about the High Street, chatting probably about boyfriends, I got bored waiting for them. So I decided to investigate a gap between the bus stop signpost which I was leaning on, and the pavement, by pushing my index finger into the hole. Unaware that my finger was there someone wiggled the signpost, which resulted in partially removing my fingernail in one fell sweep leaving me with a mangled finger underneath where the nail once was and me once again bawling my head off. Helen was left wondering how she was going to explain things when she got home, because accidents had always got to be someone's fault.

My finger took some time to heal and this meant Mother had to take me every week morning to the clinic on my way to school to have my finger dressed. The dressings were applied by a Roman Catholic nun, because the nuns were the nurses who ran the clinic; the family doctor was too busy and there were no practice nurses in those days. I was always glad when it was a Friday because I knew the dressing would not be touched again for two days and I would be free to play that evening without having to keep the bandage clean. Not that we were allowed out for too long, because there was the usual Friday routine in our house.

'It's all right for you; your mammy doesn't wash your hair every Friday.' This was the remark from Helen to her friends, who were laughing as Mother dragged her away from playing, taking her indoors for the Friday night ritual. This would start with a bath, followed by her head having to be washed with Derbac soap, after which she had to kneel and hang her wet chemical-smelling head over the newspaper that was spread open on mother's lap, there for the purpose of catching any head lice that might fall out as the nit comb was pulled through her hair.

The final straw was to be given a dose of milk of magnesium, and a cod liver oil capsule held down by a spoonful of malt. This was Mother's attempt to keep us regular, healthy and nit-free: however, hearing our friends playing outside just added to the agony. While we were of school age each of us in turn went through this ordeal, but looking back I never did have nits and kept fairly fit, apart from two occasions, one of which was when I caught the measles.

My memory of the measles is quite vivid, mainly because it affected my eyesight and I could not see for a time, so in an attempt to help me cope with the darkness that I was experiencing and to lessen my fear, a bed was made up for me to be in the living room. Here, to pacify me, Pouter my cat was put on a lead and tied to the side of the bed (poor thing) – this was because I cried every time I could not feel him nearby. The cat never did catch the measles. I remember getting out of bed and groping along the lobby on the way to the toilet and as I passed the kitchen door before reaching the bathroom, Jean and Mother were sitting at the kitchen table having a cup of tea. They had thought I was asleep, and got up, surprised that I was awake and wandering about unaided.

The other spell of sickness came on suddenly one afternoon when Helen, my cousin Betty and I had gone to the cinema and right in the middle of the film I developed a severe pain in my tummy. I could not sit still for the discomfort it caused. Betty, who had fallen asleep, refused to move when Helen tried to rouse her, this left Helen with no option but to bring me home and abandon Betty, who was older than me, to please herself.

Once I got home my mother thought at first that the pain I had might have been caused by the dye from the lollipop I had in the cinema (probably because my mouth and face were a bright purple colour from it); nevertheless she felt she had no other choice but to send for the doctor as the pain was persistent and seemed to be getting worse. After the doctor had examined me he surprised my mother by telling her my trouble was caused by a nasty attack of tonsillitis and the infection from them had travelled to my tummy glands, causing them to become enlarged and give me the bellyache.

Mother was surprised that I never complained of a sore throat or had any difficulty in swallowing, but not as surprised as Helen when Aunt Agnes (Betty's mother) came in the back door and without hesitation clipped her around the ears for leaving Betty in the cinema and allowing her to walk home by herself. Unfortunately for Helen, Aunt Agnes never waited to hear her explanation, because as soon as she had delivered her blow she left. But she reminded Helen of her wrongful deed on several occasions in the weeks that followed. Poor Helen, she always felt she never could do right for doing wrong at times: in fact this did appear to be the case a lot of the time.

One day while Mother was out – which was not very often, because I always remember her to be around somewhere; on this occasion she could have been chatting to one of the neighbours – Helen and some of her friends were sitting round the fire smoking rolled-up newspaper and acting like grown-ups. All of a sudden James Bud, the boy from the flat above who had been telling ghost stories in an attempt to try to scare the younger people there, turned and his make-believe paper cigarette touched the side of Helen's hair, setting it on fire. No doubt the chemicals from the Derbac soap helped ignite the flame. This set Helen off screaming and running around the living room in panic while everyone else tried to put out her singeing by hitting her on the head with rolled-up newspaper and cushions and anything that was at hand. Eventually the fire went out, fortunately without causing Helen to have any burns to her face or neck. But it did leave her with a crew-cut style on the one side of her head and a lot of explaining to do to Mother when she came in. As for James Bud, we did not see him for dust as he disappeared to avoid having to face the music. He never did tell us another ghost story.

2

All for a Bag of Plums

After a day of me crying and whinging with toothache, my mother, who was at her wits' end, told Helen to take me to the dentist. Helen, after moaning about having to take me when she had other things to do, reluctantly agreed – helped by the fact that Mother had given her some money as a bribe. As Helen dragged me down the road (I was five years old, she was ten), she nagged me continually, reminding me that she could be playing with her mates instead of visiting the dentist. On the way we stopped at Aitkens the greengrocers, the first shop we came to at the top of the High Street: here Helen soon parted with her money, buying a big bag of plums.

'Remember, they are all mine,' she told me. 'You won't be able to have any because the dentist will take your teeth out,' warned Helen.

When we arrived at the dental surgery (no appointment needed in those days) the dentist checked my teeth and he said to Helen, 'There is no problem, it is just her new teeth coming through which are pushing her first set out.'

Then the dentist, looking at Helen clutching the bag of plums, took the opportunity and asked her, 'Now you are here we'll have a look at you, so sit on the dental chair while I check your teeth.'

Leaving me to hold the bag of fruit Helen did as she was told and climbed on to the chair where to her shock, within no time the dentist soon removed four of her teeth. Helen could not say anything on the way back up the road because her mouth was still frozen, and when we did get home she spent the rest of the afternoon hanging over the kitchen sink spitting out blood while I stood by her side looking up at her (fascinated by the sight of her blood). For some reason or other I was now free from toothache and able to enjoy eating her plums, in between asking her if she was quite sure she did not want one before there were none left. I was unintentionally piling on the agony as Helen could see the brown paper bag reduce in size with every plum that I removed and bit into, knowing that if I did not eat them someone else would. I think this is what you call rough justice.

Growing up in Scotland, especially Lanark, taught us as children to make our own amusement. This we had to do because money was in short supply in our household and what little there was, was used on the main essentials such as food and clothing. Even then when it came to clothing, as a family we had to take our turn. One week it would be Helen that needed something to wear and the following week it might be me or Richard. Mother would buy our school uniform (which was compulsory) from a catalogue and the payments were collected weekly by a salesman knocking on the door, unsure if he would be paid or not that day.

At the beginning of one school term I felt pleased as punch having my new grey pleated skirt. But because Helen had received her skirt a few weeks earlier she was not happy and decided she needed another new skirt, so she took her two-week-old skirt and sat on the side lawn cutting up every single pleat – paid for or not. No wonder my mother chased her round the house, threatening her with the broom, until Helen escaped by hiding under the bed where Mother could not reach her.

Our family was just an ordinary family, perhaps not as well off as our neighbours. There were four of us to keep now that John had joined the Navy and Nancy was working in London: with Margaret now working and bringing in a modest salary, Mother coped as best she could. Despite the shortage of money, Mother would go each week to Lanark Auction Market where she could not resist buying something or other – who could blame her? after all she had to have some pleasure in life. Knowing this, every auction day we would hurry home from school to see what Mother had bought that day, too young to be aware that the week ahead would be a struggle financially because of the latest purchase.

One day we came home from school to find we were the proud owners of a musical organ. The fact that no one could play it, and there was certainly no hope of having lessons, did not matter – none of our friends had one, and as far as I can remember we had never before owned anything no one else had. However, the organ was short-lived at our house, because when Margaret got home from work she reasoned with Mother, asking her what made her buy the organ. Mother in turn persuaded her that the organ was for a family down the road who were less fortunate than us, and before too long it was given to them, even if they did need the basic essentials more than they needed a tune. That was typical of Mother, she would give away her last when she usually always needed it herself, just to see the pleasure on someone's face. The children that received the organ had great delight in trying to thump out a note, but I can't say their neighbours were too thrilled about having to put up with the din that came from the household as each member of the family had to have a turn at banging out a would-be tune in the hope that they might have a hidden talent that needed discovering.

Most of our amusement as children was in the form of outdoor games such as rounder with our mates, or ringing doorbells and running away before the person answered the door: sometimes it would be playing out at the auction market on a Sunday when it was closed to the public – the market, where the characteristic octagonal auction rings were a prominent landmark within the town, was situated about a mile from our house. One Sunday Helen and I with five of our friends were looking for something to occupy us. At the time we were standing at the boundary wall of the market, when one boy in the group dared us to jump off the market wall – which was between 8 and 10 feet high – into the heap of straw on the other side of the wall in the grounds of the market.

On our side of the wall there were large boulders that enabled us to climb and reach the top of the wall, and there one by one we plucked up courage to jump into the heap of straw below. There could have been any kind of dangerous implement buried in the straw, unknown to us, because the farmers from around Lanarkshire came to Lanark Market to trade and inevitably odd bits and pieces were left behind, and on occasions some broken farm equipment was dumped there. Fortunately for us, although we did not think it at the time, an unknown guardian angel passing by saw the danger in what we were doing and told the police: in those days there was always a bobby on the beat in and around the neighbourhood.

The next thing we were aware of was that the local bobby had the seven of us lined up against the wall we had climbed, and with his notebook and pen in hand pretended to take down our details. The policeman in his sternest voice asked, 'What's your name?'

'Baggy Neil,' replied our Helen defiantly.

'What's your name?' he asked me before I could answer from my terrified state.

Helen answered for me: 'Her name is Baggy Neil too.'

So it was, as the policeman questioned along the line of seven, that each one in turn gave the same answer, 'Baggy Neil.'

The bobby, trying to keep his face straight, finished by saying, 'Right, I know who you are, and if I see any of you here again I will be up to your parents letting them know. Now clear off.'

Needless to say I don't ever remember going back to the auction market to play again, at least not on a Sunday when it was closed.

Not to be outdone, we had our night adventures. For example there was the night we went to scrump for apples: the tempta-tion proved too great when we saw all those unwanted apples lying in the garden of one of the large Victorian villas at the corner of Hyndford Road before turning into Lanark Grammar

School, where we would pass the abandoned fruit each day on our way to school. Helen and her two friends planned to return one evening and pick up the best of the apples that lay abandoned. However, because I was the youngest, Mother instructed Helen (much to her reluctance) to look after me while we were out playing, so this meant that this particular evening I would have to be dragged along.

Before we set off on our daring adventure I was warned by my big sister to keep this a secret from Mother, or anyone else for that matter. We were both wearing our new windcheaters which proved to be the ideal garment for collecting apples.

When we arrived at the orchard we each in turn climbed over the stone wall surrounding the garden, and there in the dark we picked up apple after apple, pushing them into our jackets until we could only just manage to zip them up.

Heavily laden down with apples, which made us look more like Michelin Men, created a problem in climbing back over the wall. Some of us just fell over, losing our balance with the extra weight in front. As the saying goes, 'the forbidden fruit is the sweetest', but in this case forbidden fruit was not the sweetest: the apples we had acquired were none other than cooking apples. Nevertheless, on our way home we bit into the hard bitter fruit, and when we reached the top of our cul-de-sac, just around the corner and out of sight of our kitchen window, we sat on the fence to devour the remaining apples before going home.

Once home Helen, who appeared to have eaten more than the rest of us, was awake in the night with acute bellyache and let us and the world around know, so much so that Mother thought Helen had appendicitis and sent Richard my brother to fetch the doctor.

Dr Glaster, the family doctor, eventually arrived and after examining Helen (who by now thought she was dying) turned to her accusingly, not pleased that he had been fetched out of bed, and asked, 'What have you been eating?'

Helen, who was so afraid, confessed to the green apples and

by now felt that not only was she going to die, but having stolen them she would probably die in prison. Instead, once the doctor had left the house she finished up with a clip around the ear from Mother and all sympathy was withdrawn as the family returned to bed, leaving Helen to suffer in silence.

Suffering in silence was not something that Helen usually did, as was the form early one Sunday morning when she had earache and decided she would give the rest of us, including the neighbour's living in the flat above, heartache. So she sat at the open window in the bedroom and shouted in panic.

'There is a wasp in my ear I can hear it buzzing' she screamed.

'Nellie! Will you shut that wean up? And let us get some sleep.' Mrs Bud shouted to Mother from above, at the same time as banging on our ceiling with a broomstick to get her point across. The additional noise added to the commotion going on in our flat that morning. Of course there was no wasp in Helen's ear, it was an infected ear drum – but convincing her was another matter.

Helen had a thing about wasps; there was the time during her school holidays where in an effort to help Mother out financially she got paid for picking strawberries (there were a lot of fruit farms along the Clydeside), and one day during her morning break she was eating a jam sandwich when suddenly she started dancing around, yelling in pain. A wasp had got into the sandwich and stung her inside her mouth. Helen came home from the fruit fields that evening with red eyes and a swollen face which made her look as if she had a gum boil, and blaming the jam sandwiches for her sorry sight.

We never knew what Helen would do next. One night I woke to see what I thought were car headlights coming towards me, yelling out, 'Help! Stop that motor.'

'Be quiet,' said Helen.

'What are those red lights and that smell?' I panicked

'It's alright,' Helen reassured me.

But I would not be pacified and continued to call out that I could smell burning.

14

'You'll wake everyone up,' she urged.

When I sat up in bed and rubbed my eyes to enable me to focus properly, I could see Helen at the bottom of the bed with her friend Estelle. Both of them were smoking cigarettes and as they inhaled, the red ash at the end of the cigarettes had looked like car lights to me in the dark. No wonder she was telling me to be quiet: she did not want my mother to catch her smoking or to find her friend Estelle staying the night when she should be at home.

Helen worked as a 'clippie' on the buses and was so well known by her regular passengers that when she was on the early morning shift, the passengers would get on at the various bus stops and ring up their own fares on her ticket machine while Helen slept (she never was a morning person). If the inspector was at any of the stops doing a random check, the bus driver would ring the bell in order to wake Helen to warn her that the inspector was about to get on. With the help of passengers and colleagues she never did get caught.

In the years that Helen travelled back and forward on those buses she met some unsavoury characters, especially on a Friday or Saturday late shift when some of the teddy boys would get on her bus coming back from some late night dance having had too much to drink. But thankfully she was always able to deal with them in her own assertive way – usually one of her looks, or the threat of getting bashed on the head with her ticket machine, quietened the rabble.

I remember one of Helen's looks one day as I walked down the road with her; I was going to wave her off as she was on her way to catch her bus to start one of her late shifts.

'Did you make up my sandwiches?' she asked

'Aye,' I answered.

'What did you put on them?'

'Tomatoes.'

'Did you slice them up before you put them on the bread?'

'Aye,' I nodded.

15

'What did you do that for? The bread will be all soggy,' she shouted.

Then I got 'the look' just before her bus pulled up and she jumped on. I turned and walked back up the road to the house thinking about that soggy bread.

Helen and her gift for entertaining could be attributed to living in Lanark, which meant that when we as children were not making our own entertainment, some of the many local traditions would do it for us. One local tradition included Whippity Scourie which is celebrated annually on 1st March unless that day falls on a Sunday, in which case it is postponed for 24 hours to the Monday, adding to the unique identity of our Royal Burgh.

The custom is a relic of pagan times and goes back to around 1753 to celebrate the advent of spring, following a custom that is said to date back to a time when prisoners were whipped as they moved around, beating out the evil spirits and the coldness of winter at the same time as welcoming the warm start of spring. We as children eagerly looked forward to the first chimes of the church bells at 6 p.m. which gave us the signal to start beating the living daylights out of each other with balls of newspaper tied to a length of string. There was quite an art to making the perfectly packed newspaper mace, because the weapon had to survive some pretty severe treatment. Some more than others, because I know in previous years my brother John along with some of his pals would put a stone in the centre of the paper ball to clout any of the neighbouring New Lanark School pupils that entered the race: no doubt they in turn did the same as our toerags.

We would line up in a circle outside St Nicholas Parish Church in all weathers, where we had to complete three laps around the church in a clockwise direction while thumping each other with our weapons. The race was carried out in stages, with the youngest running first. At the end of the race the winner received a sum of money and loose change was thrown into the air, leaving the other children scrambling for a handful of pennies thrown by members of the Town Council; today the amount thrown could be a much as £100, all in pennies.

There are many things typical of Lanark, but some have become long-established institutions; one of the most exciting traditions is held in June, with the Lanimer Celebrations. The origins of the Lanimers date back to the twelfth century when the town was established as a Royal Burgh, and then the burgesses were instructed by the King to check the Marches and boundary stones of the Burgh annually and report on their condition; these boundaries of the land were called Landmarches, now known as Lanimers.

This occurs on the Monday, the start of Lanimer week when we as children would follow the Lord Cornet accompanied by his council predecessors, members of the Town Council (who were on horseback) who set out from the Council Chambers to ride the Marches to the boundary, where money was thrown into a shallow stream and we would paddle in to retrieve it. The Lanimer Ball takes place the following evening and the main day of celebrations is held on the Thursday when the children from all the schools in Lanark form part of the procession around the gaily decorated town in pageant floats. The bells ring and the pipe bands, tableaux and the Lanimer Queen Elect circle the town twice, ending the procession at the steps of St Nicholas Church under the magnificent statue of William Wallace situated on the steeple

Each year prior to the event, work takes place to construct a stairway beneath the feet of Wallace. This also provides a seating area large enough to accommodate the 'Queen's Court' and the people taking part on the pageant floats.

This temporary seating and stairway is built on the area directly in front of the church, hiding the main part of the building, thus leaving the steeple with Wallace's statue to form the focus point of the crowning of the Lanimer Queen, held at the bottom of the town.

The Lanimer Queen is an honour both for her and her school,

as the one chosen to represent Lanark on such a day has been elected by the school pupils as being the most popular girl in school. Her dress, shoes and jewellery worn that day are a gift from the local traders, and are displayed in their shop windows for a week prior to Lanimer Day. The cars and their chauffeurs that are used to drive the royal party in the procession are also on loan as a gift from the local car showrooms, serving a double purpose – the second being the opportunity to advertise their goods.

This was a great day for us as children – Apart from having a holiday from school, we would have a new outfit for the occasion and this alone made us feel special, although the buzz of excitement affected adults and children alike as we saw for the first time the various decorated floats and the imaginative themes, all of which had been kept a closely guarded secret from the other competitors for months during the preparation, inspired by the hope of winning first prize (awarded before the procession starts).

The morning would be taken up with the inspection and judging of the floats which after parading behind the many colourful pipe bands ended up with the crowning of the Queen at 11 a.m. Later the procession would meet at the park in Lanark where fun would be had by all; the afternoon was taken up with the Highland events which took place at Lanark Race Course on the outskirts of the town. The Town Hall concert would be held in the evening when the partakers of the procession took to the stage to perform their much-rehearsed song and dance routines. One Lanimer year our Margaret was on a float, and she had to sit on the stage dressed like an old lady while one of the boys from her school, who was dressed like an old man, sang to her, 'When you and I were young Maggie'. He was supposed to kiss her as part of the act, but she did not allow it.

Unfortunately, one year my niece Cathleen had chickenpox on Lanimer Day, but rather than her having to miss the highlight of the year Jean (her mum), in an attempt to camouflage Cathleen's very many spots, put a headscarf on her. The action highlight-ed the problem rather than hiding it, defeating the purpose, because the fact that it was the month of June and rather warm made people look at this young girl with her head wrapped up. Although I do remember we had a great view of the procession that year, probably because the crowd took a double-take at Cath-leen as she approached before they moved aside, clearing the path to avoid catching the chickenpox virus; their reluctance to get too near proved to be to our advantage. After the procession the family would enjoy a special lunch before heading out to the race course to take part in the sports and other events laid on for the afternoon; Lanimer Day was the next best thing to Christmas Day in our household.

One Christmas, Helen decided that for this particular year, our family would be no different from the other families in the neigh-bourhood. She was determined that we would have a Christmas tree. In the past years, a Christmas tree had never been at the top of my mother's list; providing a Christmas meal for us took first priority. The second priority was to have enough money to be able to buy a modest gift for each member of the family.

So it was of no surprise that Mother had no idea about Helen's intentions, and naturally thought Helen was going on night shift, when she left home that evening. However, instead of Helen having her clippie machine tucked under her coat, she was struggling to hide the only saw Mother possessed; fortunately, it was blunt.

Once Helen had turned the corner of the cul-de-sac, she (as previously planned) met up with her friend Estelle, who had the same idea of obtaining a tree, and was armed (unknown to him) with her father's axe. Together they set off into the dark, and headed for the nearest wood. When they reached the wood, and had selected the fir trees of their choice, they set about the mammoth task of cutting the trees down. This task proved to be harder than either of them had anticipated, and was not made any easier by the fact that Helen's blunt saw could not have cut butter, let alone a solid tree trunk.

Eventually, after much sweat, and toil and taking what seemed like hours to complete, the weary teenagers managed to hack down two trees. Estelle's tree was a small one, easier for her to cope with, whereas Helen had picked and chopped down the biggest tree she could find. This left her with an additional problem of how to get it home. After mustering up all the strength they could find, they struggled, and helped each other to drag the trees along the road.

Suddenly, in the distance the lights of a car headed towards the teenagers, who in a panic pulled and pushed the fir trees over a wall, before jumping over themselves, to hide until the car had passed.

'That's it,' said Estelle, 'let's leave the trees here and get home.'

'No,' said Helen, 'We have got this far; we are going to have a tree this Christmas.'

So without any more disagreement, they summoned up their remaining energy and dragged the trees to their own respective homes. When Helen got home, the next problem she had to deal with was where to put the tree. By this time it was well past midnight, and Mother and everyone else was fast asleep in bed.

Helen soon solved her problem by pushing the huge tree into the 'coal house' (this was a large walk-in cupboard in the kitchen next to the pantry). But because the tree was so tall, she had to push it in at an angle, and squeeze the branches in to enable her to close the door. Now at last she could retire to bed knowing she had achieved her ambition.

Mother got up the next morning, and routinely went to make up the fire to heat the house before she woke us. When she opened the coal house door, she was shocked to have the branches of a very large fir tree spring out at her. She quickly dashed into the bedroom and shook Helen awake. 'Where did you get that tree?' she demanded. 'We will have the polis at the door.'

Helen struggled out of bed, to drag, once again (this time with Mother's help), the tree which was now covered in coal dust out of the coal house.

'We can't take it out the front door,' said Mother, 'the neigh-bours will see us.'

So they pulled it through the lobby, and out the back door. Helen set about cutting the tree in half, because it was too tall for the living room, while Mother fetched a bucket and filled it with soil. Together they planted the tree in it and carried it back into the house where it took over the living room, and the tree, still too tall, bent over as it touched the ceiling.

At least we could say we had a Christmas tree, even though it only had a few homemade paper chains on it.

Mother need not have worried about what the neighbours thought, because Mr Bud the neighbour in the flat above us, had himself caused a stir one Christmas. One year he bought a live cockerel from the Wednesday auction market, and as Christmas day was on the following Sunday, he had to think where he could keep the live bird for three days until Christmas Eve, when it would be killed and prepared.

The only solution he could come up with was to keep the bird in the bath. So, to prevent the bird from escaping, he tied one of its legs to the bath tap. The noise and commotion that poor cockerel created in the three days leading up to Christmas gave everyone heartache as well as headache until eventually it was put out of its misery, ending up as Mr Bud's Christmas dinner.

3

Peggy's Wooden Leg

Nancy, my elder sister by 14 years, enjoyed life to the full. She would stand in front of the mirror above the fireplace in the living room putting on her make-up in preparation for the dancing held at Lanark Loch. There was never any doubt that she would stand out from the crowd, with her bright hand-knitted sweaters: she had one jumper which was made up from four coloured squares in red, yellow, blue and black, and at the same time she would wear her headscarf covered in signatures which were embroidered in different colours. But it was not the splash of rainbow colours that enticed the boys to take her on the dance floor: her dark hair, blue eyes, and natural beauty kept her dancing all night long.

One day when Nancy and her friend were coming home from the factory where they worked, my Aunt Agnes who had been looking out of her window for Nancy passing by (Aunt Agnes just lived around the corner from us), called Nancy to come to her house. As she approached Aunt Agnes told her, 'Your father is dead.'

Nancy walked in a daze down the path to her waiting friend.

'What did she say to you?' her friend asked, anxiously.

'She says my father is dead,' said shocked Nancy.

They walked in silence up the road, and as Nancy turned into our cul-de-sac our house door flung open and Richard raced out to Nancy, throwing his arms around her waist crying, 'My daddy's dead.'

Nancy, comforting him and still trying to take it in herself, led him back home away from the onlooking neighbours.

Nancy describes Father as a man who loved his children, who

would come home after a hard-working day and go on his hands and knees to let his bairns ride him like a horse. Now he would no longer be around.

After the death of my father, Nancy announced to my mother that she was finishing with her job at the factory which was within walking distance in the village of New Lanark and going into service along with her friend Annie Brown as housemaid to one of the gentry in their grand house at Coulter near Bigger just outside Lanark. No sooner the word than the deed, and Nancy bade farewell to the factory folk and moved into 'The Big House'. It was here that the girls would have the time of their life when the owners went out for the day; Nancy and her friend Annie would grasp the moment by dressing up in the lady of the house's clothes, living out their own fantasies, before biking around the grounds, enjoying their free time.

One day on such an occasion when the girls had the house to themselves, they were coming down the grand staircase dressed in the owner's clothes when, to their shock, the lady of the house returned and caught them scampering back upstairs. After a time Nancy was summoned to the drawing room. Thinking she was going to be fired, she prepared herself for the worst. Instead the lady of the house stated she would be calling to see Mother.

After her visit to our house and having a talk with Mother she returned, and once again called Nancy into the drawing room where she asked her why Nancy had not told her of my father's recent death and the situation at home. Nancy, who felt that it was none of her boss's business, told her so, and by doing so knew it was time to move on from this employment to seek greater things. There was no holding her down as Nancy has always been one for an adventure (and still is): both she and Annie left the big house and decided to seek their fortune in London.

For Nancy to visit London was a big thing in our family, never mind live there, so it was not surprising that on occasion there would be great excitement when the postman delivered a parcel from my big sister Nancy who had gone to work in the capital of England all those miles away. Helen and I would wait in anticipation as my mother opened the brown paper to reveal the box containing the goodies – something for everyone. On one such occasion I was delighted with my present, a pair of tartan boots with the zip up the front, and I wore them with pride up and down the street until some kind soul stopped me one day and asked why I was wearing my slippers. Not having had any before I never knew they were slippers, so that soon put an end to me parading the high street in my bright footwear.

The disappointment was soon forgotten with the arrival of yet another one of Nancy's parcels. Helen and I were so excited we could not wait until Mother opened it, so we set to and started to rip off the thick brown paper, revealing a cardboard box with a terrible odour. In our shock and disgust we yelled, 'What is that terrible smell?', shooting backwards and holding our noses, watching Mother who was laughing so much she could not answer us.

Nancy had sent us a pair of Arbroath Kippers which had taken their time in reaching us. Needless to say we took quite a bit of persuading before we would eat them, although it was not something we had to do more than once. In fact the parcels did not continue for much longer, because Nancy was soon to marry her Gordon and would have her own home to provide for. Her wedding took place in Lanark and I had the delight of wearing a pretty stick-out dress as a flower girl. After the reception I remember being in the foyer of the hotel busily collecting up bits of the coloured confetti that had been thrown earlier. Then as I looked up I saw Nancy and Gordon leaving and about to go into a waiting taxi. Dropping the confetti I ran to her, crying. 'Nancy, don't go with that man.'

Someone intervened and held me back to allow Nancy to escape and get off on her honeymoon with her handsome new husband.

About a year after the wedding I had a spell of sickness when I complained of non-stop bellyache. I was taken by Mother to the doctor's, where after an examination he sent me into the Law Hospital to have my appendix out. Now the Law Hospital was a 15-minute bus ride from Lanark and in those days the visiting hours were limited, especially in the children's ward where the rules were very strict. Knowing that she would not be able to get in to see me very often, Mother bribed me to stay by giving me a box of Maltesers when she said cheerio, leaving me on the ward so delighted with the chocolates that I went to the nurses' duty room to offer them one.

I was only eight and did not have the sense to know that the Maltesers might be confiscated for my own good, to my shock a nurse took the box from me saying she would keep them for me. She did keep them, but not for me – I never got them back. It was the first box of chocolates I had ever had just for myself so it was not surprising I was more upset about losing my chocolates than I was about losing my appendix.

I recovered well from my operation and the day I had my stitches out I remember bouncing up and down on the hospital bed, feeling pain-free, because up until then the stitches had pulled the skin and once they were out the relief was great. I remember getting out of bed to play with the large doll's house that sat on a table in the middle of the ward, and wishing I had one at home. Although I do remember there was a doll's house at our house at some stage of my childhood, one that Uncle Tam had made for someone in the family. The light bulbs in the rooms of the doll's house were the little bulbs you find in a torch and I remember being fascinated to see the lights come on, operated by a switch Uncle Tam had fixed on the base of the house.

Later that same year Nancy's in-laws (who I called Aunt Elsie and Uncle Norman) came to Lanark from Darwen in Lancashire for a holiday. At the end of their two-week stay with some friends they asked my mother if they could take me back to Darwen for a few weeks. My mother was not too keen at first but eventually allowed it, knowing that Nancy, who lived with them in Lancashire had just had her first-born Elaine – my new niece – and that I might be of some help to her. She could bring me back with her to Scotland when she planned to visit the family with her new baby.

My two-week holiday lasted six months, during which time I

enjoyed my new school in Darwen and my new friends I had made there, although I was totally unaware that my mother was fretting that she would not get me back. She need not have worried because while Aunt Elsie was looking after me she was very good to me. She would give me a shilling a week pocket money, but on a pretence of having earned it I had to do a bit of dusting around an already spotless house.

I remember the different way of life in Darwen compared with that in Lanark. For example, nearly everyone wore wooden clogs going to work or school, and the noise they made on the cobbled streets as the people bustled on their way sounded like a lot of horses trotting. As in Lanark it was the custom in Darwen at Halloween for the children to wear fancy dress and be prepared to carry out some form of party piece on the neighbours' doorsteps once the door had been opened to them: in return they would be rewarded for the entertainment they had provided.

As a child I had never heard of 'trick or treat.' Instead we said, 'The sky is blue the grass is green, now please may we have our Halloween?'

However the night of Halloween in Darwen was one to remember when I went with my friend to a neighbour's house who owned a shop that sold fur coats, and as we recited our poem we waited in anticipation for the wonderful gift we would receive from such a wealthy lady. You can imagine our faces when she handed us an egg each to cook for our breakfast the next day. We both walked away disappointed as we tried to carry the egg back home without breaking it – after all we could not stuff it in our pocket and go on to the next house.

The night of 5th of November was especially good fun as all the children in the street gathered around the bonfire and each of the neighbours joined in with the community spirit and produced their own special home cooking – toffee apples, treacle toffee, biscuits, etcetera, which was shared with all around the bonfire, watching the fireworks.

It was at Christmas in Darwen that I received my nurse's outfit.

At eight years old I still believed in Santa Claus – until that night, because as I lay there unable to sleep for excitement, I heard Aunt Elsie come up the stairs whispering to Norma, her teenaged daughter, 'Put it at the bottom of her bed and don't make a noise.'

I lay there wondering why they had come into the room and not put the light on, but I was too tired to speak. They fumbled at the bottom of the bed for a few minutes before leaving the room and closing the door, where once again in the dark I just nodded off to sleep. In the morning the first thing I saw, sticking out of a very full sack tied to the bedpost, was a nurse's outfit with a smart blue and white striped uniform. Little did I know then that many years later I would wear a similar outfit in a professional manner.

I remember that when I eventually went back to school in Lanark it was with an English accent, which I was unaware of, but my classmates took the Mickey because they thought I was showing off by pretending to talk differently. During one lesson the class were in an uproar, when I was asked to spell 'running' and I said 'R-U-double-N-I-N-G', the English way, where as the Scottish would say 'R-U-N-N-N-I-N-G'. I could not understand what I had said to cause such mockery and wished I was still in Darwen and hung my head and tried to hold back the tears. At that point the teacher stepped in and rebuked the class and explained that was how they spoke in England. It was not only my classmates who thought I was putting on the English accent: Richard laughed and told Mother to tell me to stop acting it, as I chatted around the house with this new-found English twang. My brother just could not believe that I was not fooling around, because he was always one for playing a joke.

When Richard left school he worked as an apprentice mechanic at a garage in Lanark. In the evening he would come home exhausted from a hard day at work, and flop in the chair by the fire still wearing his heavy-duty boots, too weary to take them off. Richard, having a good sense of humour, was always ready to play one of his jokes and usually it was on me. He would sometimes ask me to kneel at his feet while he placed his feet on my shoulders and close his eyes, pretending to sleep. I would sit as still as I could, trying to be patient and balance those heavy boots one on each side of my head without me falling over, which never happened because Richard was only playing by teasing me and making me earn my reward which would be a sixpence that I could not wait to spend. So once my big brother parted with his money I would run up through the housing estate to Patterson's – this was the name of the couple that had converted part of their house into a shop that sold most things and stayed open late hours.

'Bring me some liquorice and a tin of baked beans,' Richard would say, giving me the money, before I fled to see what I could spend my sixpence on. This was not the only time Richard would give me some of his hard-earned wages: he would sometimes slip me a shilling so that I could go to the cinema with my friend Milly Morgan who lived around the corner from us. As she was the youngest and only girl in her house, Milly was spoilt by her older brothers and wanted for nothing so it was great for me to have that shilling and feel equal as we set off together to the Regal Cinema, the only one in Lanark.

I remember being in awe of Richard's girlfriend Margaret (later to become his wife). She would come from Kirkfieldbank to see my mother and as she turned into our cul-de-sac all heads would turn as this tall, dark-haired attractive lady wearing a yellow swagger coat walked to our door.

'That's our Richard's girlfriend,' I would boast to my friends.

Later in life Richard had to do his National Service in the Royal Air Force. This meant he had to leave Scotland to serve a lot of his time at the Halfpenny Green Base near Bridgnorth, Shropshire. Being away from home did not appeal to Richard so every chance he had to come home he took. Because the fare from Shropshire to Scotland was too expensive it meant he had to depend on hitchhiking, and this he managed to do travelling on the back of anything that could move as long as it was heading north. Probably the fact that he was courting Margaret at the time gave him the incentive to reach home. Richard was quite pleased to complete his service, if only to get back to his home-land and his Margaret. Meanwhile, back at home, Mother was pleased to see him back amidst his 'ain folk'.

Little could he have imagined that he would be going back to Bridgnorth again many years later when his sisters were married and lived in Shropshire, and he would visit Halfpenny Green. Except, instead of a airfield, it was the outdoor market. There his brother-in-law Jack asked a stall holder whether there was a full set of the cup and saucer he was looking at, even although the cup was the size of a baking bowl and was intended to hold fruit, instead of several gallons of tea. The saucer was the size of a car wheel, and it was doubtful there was a table large enough to hold a set of six of the cups and saucers never mind anything else. The very question left Richard reeling with laughter. No, he could not have foreseen that when he packed his bag to come home and prepare for his church wedding.

Church was not a place that was frequented much by Mother. In fact, I never remember my mother going to church other than for a wedding, although she did encourage my sister Margaret, who was a regular visitor of the Mission, to take Helen and me along to Sunday School – not just once on a Sunday, but twice. We would go at 11 a.m. to the Mission Hall, which was built in 1838 as a school for the poor during that period; the hall was in the Broomgate situated at the bottom of the High Street in Lanark which today has been converted into luxury flats.

Once we reached the Mission Hall we had to climb a spiral staircase to the top. I loved the children's choruses I was taught there and the Bible stories that the Sunday School teachers told us. We would leave there just in time for 1 p.m. when we would go to the Baptist Sunday School in St Leonard Street at the top of the High Street. This was a wee tin church, and as I recall it was always full; the Sunday School was held in the back room of the church, taking place after the main service.

Yet again I enjoyed more Bible stories and was taught the actions to apply to the many choruses we sang each week, some of which I have never forgotten to this day. One favourite related to the Bible story (Luke, chapter 19, verses 1 to 10) about Zacchaeus, a rich tax collector who was a little man disliked by the people he had swindled. The chorus went like this:

> **Zacchaeus** was a very little man
> And a very little man was he
> He climbed up into a sycamore tree
> For the Saviour he wanted to see
>
> And as the Saviour passed that way
> He looked up to the tree
> And said now Zacchaeus you come down
> For I am coming to your house for tea.
>
> Chorus:
> Oh yes oh yes I am coming to your house for tea.

The tune was catchy, and all the Sunday School children would stand up and act out the actions with great delight.

Another favourite was the chorus that made us all feel equal, no matter what we looked like or what our background was, or even how much we could afford to put in the collection plate. This was the 'Clean Hands or Dirty':

> Clean hands or dirty hands
> Brown eyes or blue
> Pale cheeks or rosy cheeks
> Jesus loves you
>
> Come to Him while you may
> He will wash your sins away
> Clean hands or dirty hands
> Brown eyes or blue

In recent years I copied these choruses out, along with many more, for a friend who was visiting a missionary school in Sierra Leone and needed some more new material to teach the children in Sunday School there. I could imagine their little shiny black faces beaming with delight as they sang the joyful songs, bringing to life the words in II Corinthians, chapter 6, verse 10. '*As sorrowful, and yet always rejoicing; as poor, yet making many rich; as having nothing, and yet possessing all things.*' It was good to think that these children so far away, who had very little in the way of worldly wealth, would be singing the same songs I had enjoyed as a child.

Even although my mother found it difficult to make her money stretch, she would always give me what she could afford to put in the collection plate. Many a time my friends would stop at the sweet shop on the way to Sunday School and spend some of the money they had been given to put in the collection. I never had enough to do that, but even so I used to think it was God's money and would have been afraid to use it other than for what it had been given for. One Sunday I went to the Baptist Church with nothing more than two halfpennies. I was not too bothered because I thought I could make the two coins jungle as I dropped them in the plate to make it sound like more; but to add to my shame the Pastor announced it was a special collection that week and that there would be a second gift collection for the mission field, therefore there would be two plates going round.

I will never forget how mortified I felt sitting in church, silently ashamed that I would have to put a halfpenny in each plate, hoping that no one would see me do so. Little did I know at that young age that it was not the amount of money that I gave that mattered to God. He is the One who provided for me as I discovered the greatest riches I was to obtain was the wealth of becoming a Christian at an early age. I think I was about ten or eleven when guided by my older sister Margaret I committed my life to the Lord. I was to experience a wealth of untold riches to be bestowed upon me, as I sought to serve Him.

At 5 a.m. each morning while we slept my mother would walk a mile or more in all weathers to one of the local farms to milk the cows. She would be back in time to give us our breakfast before sending us off to school. One morning she arrived at the farm where, to her horror, she found a dead calf. For some strange reason she feared she might be blamed for its death, so in a state of panic she decided she would bury it. She hurriedly set to and covered it over with straw in the hope that someone else would find it. All too soon the farmer did find it, which was not at all surprising, because as he came around the corner there to greet him were four hoofs sticking up in the air from the heap of straw that half covered the calf's head and body.

'What's happened here, Nellie?' he asked.

'Well, I found it like that and thought you might think I did it,' replied my frightened mother.

'No woman, these things happen on farms,' he said, much to my mother's relief. She had thought she might lose her job because of it: unfortunately, that is not what she did lose. Instead, it was during one of her milking sessions that a cow kicked her on the right leg, and because Mother was never one to make a fuss and just got on with things she ignored getting her leg seen to until the discomfort was more than she could tolerate. She had to give in despite her pride, and go and see the doctor, who confirmed that the outcome of the kick had caused a clot in her leg. Sadly, two years later, this resulted in her having to have an above-knee amputation of her right leg, drastically changing my mother's life completely. Now she could no longer provide for her family, but would have to depend on others.

So it was arranged that when she came home from hospital John, Jean and Cathleen my niece would leave their home, which was outside Lanark in the village of Auchanheath, to move in to care for her and look after me. Although Richard and Helen were still living at home they were now both working, and I was to do my share of helping at home after school when needed.

It was during these hospital visits that the nurses that were caring for mother made a lasting impression on me. I remember how kind they were to the patients as they bustled around the ward in their white starched aprons, tucking in the corner of the beds as they passed. I knew then that I wanted to become a nurse.

One of the ways I was able to contribute in an effort to help at home was to make myself available at the beck and call of one of the neighbours. By running her errands after school I could earn some pocket money, even though this would involve going a distance of a mile there and back to the shop, very often more than once on the same afternoon because Mrs MacPhee would have forgotten to ask me to get something or other. All this effort and energy was for the reward of 3 shillings a week. This sum of money came in useful when it was needed as part of the housekeeping, and would be borrowed if need be: otherwise I saved it each week, because my goal was to have enough for a Timex watch like some of my schoolmates had by the end of the year.

The neighbour Mrs MacPhee was a colourful character and the fact that she had a wooden leg that did not bend at the knee proved to be of little disadvantage to her: in most cases it came in useful. Like the time when she and her husband Jock had an argument and she threw him out of their front door with her wooden leg after him: it was the only thing at that time that she could find to hit him with.

Jock MacPhee was a little man, who kept pigeons in his back garden, much to the annoyance of the neighbours. Especially on a Monday when their washing was on the line. It was quite a common thing to hear Mrs Bud who lived in the flat above say to Mother, 'Jock's pigeons are flying low today Nellie.'

One night the MacPhees' teenage daughter was on her way home from the cinema and just as she got around the corner at the top of the cul-de-sac to turn down the road leading to her home, a man who had been following her up the main road must have realised she was nearly home and started to chase her. The girl, running for her life, got as far as the path leading to her front door when the man, who had caught up with her, grabbed her by the ankle causing her to land on her face yards from the front step. Her screams brought her dad to the door, but not before the man in question had fled. Jock opened the door to see his daughter lying on her belly, screaming in terror.

'Get inside you silly madam, you will have all the neighbours up,' Jock responded.

His terrified daughter's story about the man chasing her fell on deaf ears as far as her dad was concerned. He thought it was her excuse for coming home late.

There was always something entertaining happening in our cul-de-sac. One weekend the MacPhee family set out for a drive in their newly acquired banger of a car. No matter how old the car was, it the only one in the cul-de-sac at that time and therefore as they left the house for their outing they made the most of showing off to the neighbours, who were out leaning on the gates taking the event in. The neighbours were still there some 20 minutes later to view the return of the MacPhees as they came back, each carrying a piece of the car, somewhat subdued as they crept back into the house. Apart from Peggy's (Mrs Macphee) head which was still held high as she nagged little Jock at letting her down again.

However lively the neighbours were, I remember Mrs MacPhee as being kind to me even if she did have her pound of flesh by running me off my feet. Slave driver or not, she had a kind heart. I don't know if Jock thought so at times when that old leg of hers hit him on the back of his head on several occasions.

Mr Bud was one of the other neighbours who never failed to unintentionally entertain everyone. In the summer he worked in his garden and was very proud of his strawberry plot. The birds however, caused him a problem, as they attacked the ripening fruit. In an attempt to keep this from happening, he came up with a brainwave to protect his strawberries and frighten away the birds.

He hung several tin cans onto a length of string which was

then tied on to canes put in the ground surrounding the strawberry plot. This plan worked only as long as there was a breeze,
so on calm days he would carry Tina down the stairs from the
flat and put her in her wheelchair which he had placed at one
end of his plot. Giving her the loose end of the piece of string
attached to the canes, her job was to pull on the string to rattle
the cans if a bird came near the strawberries.

4

Thirteen Empty Milk Bottles

Although confined to a wheelchair Mother remained as far as possible independent. She would get herself out of her chair and onto the floor to bum her way through the hall to the toilet. Despite her physical difficulties Mother never lost her sense of humour and I remember many a time when she would just laugh, even in the most awkward situations. One of which was trying to get back into her wheelchair from the floor after one of her many bum around the house episodes, with me trying to heave her up – she was no lightweight and she would shake all over laughing as we kept slipping back on to the floor until at last we achieved the landing on the seat of that antique wheelchair.

In order to give Jean (my sister-in-law) a break from caring for Mother and at the same time allowing Mother to have a change of scenery, every so often Mother would spend the odd week or two at my sister's home in Glasgow. Margaret, Bill and their twins (just babies) lived in a large flat on the ground floor of the Soldiers' Home in Maryhill, Glasgow (Bill had been in the Army). They would travel to Lanark by train, then Bill would travel back in the goods wagon with Mother in the wheelchair; this all added to the excitement of her holiday.

During Mother's time spent in Glasgow she would sit in the window watching the happenings in the streets of Glasgow, of which there were many; when the weather was nice she would sit outside by the door of the Soldiers' Home and it was here she would meet the local children who were playing in the street.

The children would often sit on the kerb by her wheelchair and ask her questions.

'What happened to your leg missus?' asked one wee boy. 'Did it just fall off?'

Mother's eyes would water because of a problem with her tear ducts; this would cause tears to run down her cheeks.

'What's wrong with your eyes missus?'

'Are they sweating with the heat?' asked another boy.

Margaret would come out now and again to check that the children were not bothering her. Mother never complained, she loved their company and never tired of their questions: instead she always made sure she had a sweet for them or a stick of rock from Lanark, which they had to share.

Mother's wheelchair was an old-fashioned one with a canvas seat, small wheels and a wooden foot rest that could extend out if needed. Bill, when he could, would take Mother along Maryhill Road to let her window shop and have a chance to meet the locals. One busy Saturday he commented on how everyone seemed to be clearing his path to let him through, as he wheeled her along.

'Isn't this great, how considerate everyone is?' he said.

Mother could not answer him for laughing. The footrest was fully extended and unknown to Bill everyone coming in contact with it was being walloped on the back of the legs, causing them to be bounced out of the way.

While in Glasgow, just as at home, Mother would bum her way around the Soldiers' Home. One evening after a busy day with the twins, Margaret sat down with Bill having a chat, when all of a sudden Margaret gasped, 'Where is Mother?'

Realising they had not seen her for a few hours they jumped up to go and look for her. After all, how far can a one-legged woman bum herself around? They found her sitting on the bathroom floor patiently waiting for someone to open the door, because she could not reach the handle.

'Why didn't you shout, Mother?' Margaret anxiously asked.

'Oh, I am OK. I didn't want to bother you,' smiled Mother.

When Mother came back to Lanark after her two weeks in Glasgow she missed the children she had met there and things at home seemed a little quiet after the busy happenings on the Maryhill Road in Glasgow. So in fine weather sitting outside in her wheelchair alongside Tina (a relative of Mr and Mrs Bud who lived with them in the flat above and who also was confined to a wheelchair) seemed a little boring after her adventure. Knowing this made me want to do something about it, so the one and only time I took my mother out in her wheelchair came about after pleading with my sister-in-law Jean to allow me to do so.

Jean was reluctant to let me take her at first because she was concerned that Mother would be too heavy for me to push; I was eleven years old and skinny without a muscle in sight. However, I managed to convince Jean it would be no problem and eventually we set off on our walk. I remember using all the strength I could muster to push the wheelchair up the small incline from our house to the corner of the cul-de-sac where we would be out of sight of Jean who I knew was watching from the kitchen window to see how I was coping.

Once we were around the corner we set off on our adventure, me pushing and shoving, Mother smiling happily to have a change of scenery – however precarious it might turn out to be. After all she was not strapped in, and as we bumped along the road hitting every hole in sight she just bounced up and down and never complained. She had said she would like to go to the graveyard to see my dad's grave. This was not unusual, because in those days the graveyard is where most folks went for a walk, especially at a weekend, probably because the main park in Lanark was at the lower end of the town, quite a distance away. We set off down the back road past the Catholic school over the railway bridge and through the oldest surviving tollgates in Scotland (1820) into the auction market, then made our way to the gateway, the entrance of which was cobble stones. After bouncing the wheelchair over the cobbles the next challenge was to cross the main road which we mastered without getting run over, then into the cemetery.

Now the cemetery was cared for by the local council and looked more like a public park, with its well-kept grass and tidy paths. In order to reach my father's grave we had to go along the narrow path which started on the level at the top of the graveyard then sloped downwards towards a row of graves that lay horizontally along the bottom. Beyond them was the fence that separated the grounds of the graveyard from the Lanark tomato greenhouses (big business in Lanark at that time) which were behind the fence.

We got to the brim of the path which led to Dad's grave and I started to descend, but to my horror the combination of the slope, Mother's weight and the heavy canvas wheelchair was just too much for me. The chair took off. I let go, and watched in fear as it hurtled down the path at a rate of knots, where it came to a sudden stop as the front wheels hit the edge of the path, throwing Mother out and landing her in a sitting position on the first available grave with the chair on top of her. When I reached her and pulled the chair off her, there she was resting her back against the headstone of the corpse whose grave she was sitting on, laughing her head off – unhurt, or so she said.

If there ever is a time for a catastrophe to happen then this timing was perfect. The siren had just gone for the tomato workers' lunch time and they came out to the sight of this one-legged woman on top of a grave. From a distance she must have looked as if she was coming out of the grave with her one leg bent up while the other leg could have been still in the grave trying to clamber out. However it looked to the tomato workers, it was enough to shock them.

My shouts of help soon brought a group of men over the fence to my aid, and after lifting Mother back into the wheelchair they took their leave to have their lunch break, still leaving me with the problem of getting her back up the path we had come down at such speed. How I managed I don't know, but I did, and

Mother and I were sworn to secrecy never to tell Jean of our mishap just in case we decided to have another adventure: we did not want to jeopardise our chances in the future.

However, a second adventure with Mother in the wheelchair was not meant to be, because Mother took ill two days after Christmas and was taken into the Law Hospital in Carluke Lanarkshire, where she died. She must have known she was going to meet her Maker because, amazingly, it was while she was in the ambulance on her way to hospital that she made her peace with God, asking Him to forgive her for her sins, and accepting the Lord as her Saviour – proving that it is never too late to get right with God. The night Mother died, John and Jean came back from being at the hospital for several hours and had the difficult job of breaking the bad news about mother's death to the family. It was late at night and Cathleen and I were in bed, and John tried to soften the blow by coming into the bedroom and giving me Mother's wedding ring. I was 13 years old and remember the surprise of being handed her gold ring, and wondering why she had taken it off. Somehow it did not feel right. I wanted my mother, not her ring, that night – even though I was aware I had been chosen to have it.

Around the house there were still some of Mother's unopened Christmas presents that had not been touched because she had not felt well enough to be bothered opening them on Christmas day. When these gifts were eventually opened, the only present that sticks in my mind was a winceyette nightdress with a pale blue background and covered in deep blue flowers, the last parcel to be sent from Nancy who still lived in England but who now was making her way back to Scotland, having received the news that mother was so ill. At that time there were no fast motorways and public transport took a lot longer from England to Scotland, with plenty of stops throughout the journey. This all added to Nancy's distress when she discovered that Mother had died before she reached Scotland, so when she arrived at the house she was not only weary from travelling but had the added distress of not being able to say her goodbyes to Mother, who she had not seen for a while.

On the day of Mother's funeral I, with Cathleen my niece, was shipped off to the village of Auchinheath where Cathleen's granny lived and who was going to look after us for the day. Funerals in Scotland in those days were not the place for children; in fact it was only the men folk that attended the graveside while the women prepared the tea put on after the burial. After doing so the women would go to the grave later to pay their respects and see the flowers that were laid there.

That day in Auchinheath the insurance man called on Cathleen's granny as a routine call and during his visit he asked her who I was (he had seen Cathleen before). 'Oh, her mother is getting buried today', she told him.

I will never forget that feeling of loneliness, and when I went back home how empty I felt inside knowing that Mother would never be there again when I came home from school.

When I finished school I still wanted to do nursing and as there were no teaching hospitals nearby I left Lanark and went to live with Margaret, Bill and the twins in Glasgow so that I could apply to start my nurse's training at the Victoria Infirmary Hospital, one of the large teaching hospitals in the city, when I was old enough; until then I had two jobs to fill the gap years.

The first job I had was working in a small ladies' fashion shop on the Maryhill Road in Glasgow. Here my first duty in the morning was to wash the shop windows which were always filthy, caused by the splashes from the passing of the heavy traffic which included the rattling past of the old trams on their way into the city centre. Once the windows sparkled for a period however short, I would have the task of ironing the underwear and the selected number of items chosen to be displayed in the shop before being sold on to the public.

The actual selling of the items of clothing would be the privilege of the senior assistant or the owner Miss Firth. Whether that was because I was deemed too young to deal with the Glaswegian, or not to be trusted to give the right change, I am not sure. However, I became an expert in tea-making and being a general dogsbody.

The end of my career as a would-be shop assistant came when Miss Firth presented me with a very full, pleated fawn skirt, too long, too big, a hand-me-down from someone with a much larger frame than my 7 stone weight. Miss Firth told me to wear it to work; this in itself was an insult because the shop did not have its own uniform and obviously I was not dressed to her liking, even though Margaret always made sure I was presentable to the public by being clean and tidy. When I arrived home that evening I was more than a little upset at the prospect of reaching up to wash windows wearing a skirt that I could not hold onto while all of Glasgow looked on getting a good view from the tram as they travelled to work.

I moved on from this employment after Margaret visited Miss Firth to inform her that I did not need any hand-me-downs. Instead she would be walking me out of the ladies' fashion shop and perhaps Miss Firth might replace me by employing someone who would fit into the large skirt better.

Now that I had left the shop assistant experience behind, Margaret was determined I was heading for better things and encouraged me to apply for a position as junior receptionist for the Students' Representative Council at Glasgow University. Before I attended for an interview Margaret instructed me as to how I should enter and leave a room, how I should sit and address the panel, and where to place my hands – which, by the way, she had manicured in preparation for any would-be inspection.

We arrived at the gates of the university in plenty of time but not too early–I did not want to appear too keen. Margaret gave me the onceover and after making arrangements to meet me later, she headed off with the twins in the pram, leaving me to it. I entered the gatehouse of the university which then was the head-quarters of the Students' Union Association and to my surprise I felt quite relaxed once inside, faced with a group of students not much older than myself and very friendly. After waiting with the students for a few minutes, who during this time were all too occupied with fooling around and planning their next party to worry about whether or not I looked the part, with my clean face and shiny hair, and tried to make me feel at ease, an older student appeared and asked me to follow him through to another room where I was presented before a panel consisting of the president of the Union Donald McDonald, the vice-president Arthur Mc-Cartney, the secretary Mrs Williams and a medical student Peter McKay. During the interview I felt I had to tell the panel that if I did get the job I would only work there until I was old enough to apply for nursing, because that was the profession I was interested in pursuing and it was only right that they should know that. I was 17 years old at the time and could not start nurse training until I was 18. The group on the panel appeared amused at my statement and Donald McDonald told me later that it was my honesty that got me the job.

One of my first duties of the day as junior receptionist was to do the filing. The filing cabinets, along with piles of paper to be filed in them, were kept in Mrs Williams's office under her watchful eye–as was I when I carried out my task each morning. Perhaps it was just in case I should dare to read too much of the content that was on the documents I had to handle. Although this was not MI5 and only a university office I took my job very seriously, even if Mrs Williams made me feel very nervous and, because I dreaded being in her company for too long, it was a job that always seemed to take an age. This tall, slim, white-haired lady had held her position for years and because of this her word was law: well at least until she left the building, then everyone would visibly relax and the noise level would rise.

Coffee break was a ritual when I had to prepare two cream crackers and cheese (it had to be Cracker Barrel Cheese) cut at just the right thickness for her ladyship, and some mornings I would have to run to the nearest small store to buy the cheese especially ordered for her. However, apart from Mrs Williams's rigid, unchanging habits, she was good to me. In the front reception office where I worked I sat at my desk opposite Tracy, the shorthand typist. Now, Tracy was the complete opposite of Mrs Williams: she was young, short and curvy, always on a diet, and although she was married she liked to flirt with the students, which they in turn responded to – after all, she was an attractive girl, full of fun.

Influenced by Tracy I once went on a diet with her and our lunch for a week comprised of a bunch of green grapes every day. At that time I weighed 7 stone and was 5 foot 6 tall. I had no curves to speak of: in fact my first bra, which I bought when I worked in the ladies' fashion shop, was a 30AA cup and the only reason I wore it was just so I could say I had a bra. Working alongside Tracy was an eye-opener for me: she would advise me on fashion and hairstyles. Talking about hairstyles, there was a rare occasion when I arrived at work one day after just having had my hair done the previous evening: this was not something that happened very often because of the cost of hairdressers, but for some reason or other I had ventured out to impress the students that had invited me to a do that night. Although I did not seem to impress Mr MacArthur who, on his arrival at the office, gave me a surprised look, and like a true Islander (he came from the Isle of Lewis) he said what he was thinking and announced his surprise at me being so vain by having my hair done.

'Not a thing I would have expected from a Christian girl,' he announced.

His rebuke and stern look left me feeling guilty, but I did not know why – I was too naive to realise he was only joking and any vanity I might have had with my new hairstyle soon faded as a result of his remark.

My time spent at Glasgow Students' Union was one that I would not like to have missed, with all the many fun events that took place while I was there, some of which were fund raising for some charity or other that was in need. One that I remember was a challenge with the students to see how many bodies could be fitted into a Mini car. On the day of the challenge a Mini was driven to the front of the university where all the students that intended to take part gathered. I think our group managed to squeeze around 42 student bodies into the car, resulting in arms, legs, heads and other parts of the body hanging out everywhere.

On another occasion the feeling of terror and excitement all wrapped into one was never to be forgotten as I mounted the back of a powerful engine and we sped off through the streets of Glasgow. It was of course in the days before helmets were compulsory so the wind in my hair produced its own style on return to the students' union after my first experience on the back of Alistair McCormick's (a medical student) new motorbike.

As if there was not enough going on during the day at work there was always an excuse for a party at the university and I remember my first, when I was asked to bring a bottle. The 'bring a bottle' worried me because I did not drink and could not think what I could take, but I need not have troubled myself. Margaret produced a bottle of homemade ginger ale which went down a treat–either that, or the students did not notice the difference after the alcohol they had already consumed.

Like many of the students I would scan the noticeboard for odd jobs in an attempt to earn some money. As a result of searching I would often babysit for some of the professors' children to enable the professors and their wives to attend the many social functions put on at the university and elsewhere.

One night I went to a professor's home to babysit his two daughters while he took his wife to the theatre. Before leaving for their night out I was given a tour of the house which was very big – not surprising as it was one of the grand houses on the Great Western Road. In the sitting room of this big house I had been left a neat tray containing a soft drink and a tasty snack. Before the professor and his wife left they made sure the children were in bed: however that was only until they heard the front door close, then they dived downstairs and before I knew what was happening they had finished off my snack and started to practice on their violins in an attempt to entertain me – or drive me mad.

The latter was nearer the truth, so after a time of screeching music and awkward conversation with two little posh girls who thought they knew everything, I managed to persuade them to go back to bed while I took the tray into the kitchen to wash up. It was here to my surprise that I found 13 empty unwashed milk bottles lined along the window sill in a very untidy kitchen. Not at all what I would have imagined I might find in a professor's kitchen in such a well-to-do area. Back in Lanark in my younger days Mother's modest kitchen had never been in such an unkempt state as this one.

On returning home the professor walked me home through the thick Glasgow fog, telling me all about his trip to the theatre – but all I could think of was that this posh man that I had looked up to had gone down in my estimation, because I knew about his 13 dirty milk bottles.

I remember my time spent at Glasgow University as happy days, a time when I met some amazing people from all aspects of life. The experience I gained there give me a new-found confidence to start off my nursing career, together with the glowing references I received from such characters.

5

The Grey Lady

Prior to commencing my general nursing which started in September 1963 in the main hospital, the Victoria Infirmary in Glasgow, I was sent to spend three months at the Orthopaedic Hospital on the outskirts of Glasgow. This was an experience of nursing never to be forgotten; apart from the rigid way the hospital was run, the characters I got to know while working alongside of them and finding out their different ways of doing things, however strange at times they might have been, was something I would not have wanted to miss. The Orthopaedic Hospital had one long corridor with its wards branching off from it: at the end of the corridor was another corridor that ran horizontal to the main corridor and this led to the nurses' quarters. It was in these quarters that I shared a dorm with three others who I had met for the first time: they also were in the same training set as me and were to become my friends throughout my nursing life.

The old-fashioned matron who kept us in order like soldiers in an army unit ran the hospital like a military camp with rules that had to be kept: perhaps understandable as after all she had young nurses many of which, including myself, had just left home for the first time. So it was not unreasonable that it was compulsory for the nursing staff to be in by 11 p.m. with lights out, ensuring that they got a good night's rest to enable them to cope with the physical demands required of them during a working day on the wards. Mealtimes also had their rules: on entering the dining room nursing staff could not sit at the table until the matron sat down at the head of the top table where she could keep an eye everyone, so until she sat the nurses had to remain standing to attention behind their chair until the matron beckoned them to sit. There they had to stay, and they were not allowed to leave the table until beckoned by her to do so.

One scary encounter I had with Matron happened after a few weeks of me being at the hospital; I was called to the matron's office to receive my pay packet. She handed it to the nurses personally in those days – the reason she did this was to give her the opportunity to get to know the nurses and to find out how they were coping with the job. Prior to this particular day I had caught a wart virus that had left a row of small warts along the knuckles on my right hand, and in an effort to remove them I had used a caustic pencil to paint them off; however being an inexperienced young nurse I had applied too much caustic to my skin which resulted in burning some of the skin on the back of my hand. In an attempt to hide the injury I had bandaged the affected area and up until now had managed to conceal it from my senior colleagues; so as I stood before the matron I did so with one hand tucked behind my back. Thinking I had managed to get away with it, I took my payslip from her with my left hand and made for the door to escape. As I placed my hand on the door handle I could feel the matron's gaze on my back before she called me back to her desk.

She asked, 'Nurse Dickie, what have you done to your hand?'

'Oh! That?' I looked surprised as I gazed at the bandage as if for the first time. 'I was a little careless with a caustic pencil,' I replied, blushing from head to toe.

'Attend the medical room for treatment on your way out,' she ordered.

All that panic for nothing, I thought, as I left the room.

Not like the panic one nurse had one night at 'lights out' as the matron, armed with her torch, was checking the nurses' quarters. Joyce, a nurse, had just began to wash her hair (the washroom was situated in the corridor between the nurses' rooms) when she heard the matron coming. Joyce quickly put out the light and hid behind the washroom door, her hair full of soap-suds. The matron entered the washroom and shone her torch around, and the light from the torch reflected in the mirror re-vealing Joyce's white frothy head. Much to Joyce's relief the matron flew out of the washroom and down the corridor and was not seen until late the next day. You see, there was an old hospital tale relating how the ghost of The Grey Lady walked the hospi-tal corridors at night, and because The Grey Lady had suppos-edly been a nurse it was said that she particularly loitered around the nurses' quarters. Up until that night I believe the matron had pooh-poohed the story, saying it was told by some as a means to scare young nurses into keeping to 'lights out' time.

One afternoon while I was left in charge of a ward at the Or-thopaedic Hospital, Barbara (one of the nurses who shared my quarters) and I had been left instructions from the doctor to remove some surgical sutures from the lady in bed five. The doctor had not questioned our nursing abilities and although we had been taught the theory, applying the practice was another matter. Nevertheless we dutifully prepared a sterile dressing trolley and approached the patient's bedside. Unknown to the trusting patient neither Barbara nor myself had removed stitches before and both of us were eager to carry out this new task. However, we were totally unprepared for what we were about to see.

Once we unwrapped the bandages on the patient's feet we both held back the gasp of shock, although our faces must have said it all as we revealed a right and left foot with no toes. In place where the gangrenous toes had been surgically removed were a very neat row of between 30 to 40 cosmetic sutures on each foot. Quickly we composed ourselves and banished our sense of shock by chatting to the patient about everything and any-thing, in a bid to reassure her and ourselves that we knew what we were doing. Eventually, and perhaps a lot slower than ex-pected, we managed very carefully to carry out our task, even al-though it was sometime later, without any discomfort to the lady and departed her bedside rather exhausted but rather pleased with ourselves. Removing stitches since has never quite had the same thrill.

After completing our three months' orthopaedic training it was time for us to move from the countryside back to our own hospital in the city where we felt the real action was to be found, and I for one could not wait to get stuck in.

At last it was time to start my general nursing training at the Victoria Infirmary in Glasgow. The hospital, which was situated right opposite Hamden Park Football Stadium, was a large, impressive stone building from the outside, and equally as impressive inside with its long corridors and high ceilings which echoed the sound of the footsteps that walked its length. At that time (1963) there was a saying amongst the nurses in the city that:

'The Glasgow Royal Infirmary bred the ladies. The Great Western Hospital bred the workers. The Victoria Infirmary bred the nurses.' But this saying altered depending what hospital the nurses worked in who were relating it.

However, there could be no greater experience gained in Casualty at the Victoria than that of patching up the supporters of the Celtic and Rangers teams after a match on a Saturday. Casualty was where we attempted to stitch up heads, faces and any other parts of the fans' anatomy that had suffered due to the fights that had become a ritual after each match, while at the same time having to try and keep the opposite fans apart in the corridors of Casualty was a skill in itself.

Nevertheless this was not without its funny side, I remember being asked a question one Saturday night by one blood-stained man who was more than a little worse for drink.

'What team do you support nurse?'

'Oh, I'm not interested in football,' I answered, thinking I was being diplomatic.

'Ah! But if you were interested in football, which team would you support'?

To which I replied, completely changing the subject, 'Let's give you this tetanus injection you need.'

This proved to be the quickest way to sober up any would-be troublemaker.

On a different Saturday night a nine-year-old boy was brought into Casualty by his mother, and when the doctor asked her what the boy's problem was his anxious mother replied, 'Well doctor, he keeps passing out.'

After going through the usual routine examinations by the trainee doctors on duty, the boy's diagnosis appeared to puzzle them. Then after some time spent discussing between themselves what to do next the young doctors finally agreed, and the boy was asked to walk across the room. Just as I thought, the little lad could not walk straight because he was under the influence of alcohol. I had seen a few drunks in my time – after all, it was Glasgow – and the fact that you could smell alcohol on the boy's breath did provide a big clue. It turned out that the trainee doctors had suspected that the boy was drunk but were ethically treading carefully as far as the mother was concerned. His mother, who up until this time had acted vague about her son's symptoms when they had questioned her, now challenged admitted with embarrassment that her son must have drunk the dregs from the empty beer bottles left in their kitchen that night.

On another Saturday night while I was on duty in Casualty, a double-decker bus pulled up outside the Casualty entrance and within seconds the driver and his conductor rushed in rather harassed-looking saying they had an unwanted passenger. The Casualty doctor on duty that night asked a hospital porter to accompany him before he went out to look into what at first sight appeared to be an empty bus. Puzzled as to why the bus driver and conductor had brought their problem to the hospital the doctor and porter searched downstairs before going upstairs where they found sitting in the top front seat a very dead old man. Whether he had paid his fare or not we never did find out; this was just one of very many run-of-the-mill events that happened in Glasgow.

It was the 1960s the time of the bouffant hairstyle, when fashion conscious-ladies of that era would visit the hairdresser's once a week. Those that had long hair would have the popular style of the day which was at that time a bunch of curls backcombed on the top of their head looking like a bowl of fruit balancing there. During my time in Casualty one very ill fashionable lady with a pile of curls on her head was brought in complaining of severe headaches, temperature and feeling sick.

Once she had been examined and a history had been taken it turned out that her fancy hairstyle had not been disturbed for a few weeks, and she had been titivating her hair up by applying more hairspray to keep it in place. The excessive amount of lacquer caused her head to became itchy and irritated, so rather than disturb her hairstyle and risk putting it out of place she would scratch her skull by using a knitting needle through her curls.

This resulted in the woman's scalp becoming all scratched and cut by the point of the knitting needle. The outcome was that this allowed infection to get in through the broken skin, which was not helped by the constant use of lacquer applied to her hair, causing the infection to spread. The damaged skin on her scalp provided an area which had produced a perfect place for bugs to breed, one of which was a beetle which had eaten its way into her scalp, causing a great deal of damage to her health. Fortunately for her, that damage was rectified in time by the aid of medical intervention and the use of antibiotics.

Some cases that came through the doors of Casualty were more dramatic than others, and these were the people that would not be forgotten easily. One day a man was rushed through the corridors on a stretcher and had to be taken without delay straight to theatre where a team of surgeons were waiting having been alerted that he was coming. I caught sight of the patient as he travelled through the unit and could see that his head was all misshaped. Apparently his head had been caught in a hydraulic machine at work, and the chances of the poor soul surviving were very slim. It needed nothing short of a miracle to pull him through. Sights like this were fortunately rare – surprisingly, because health and safety on the factory floor was not as stringent as it is today; there were too many avoidable accident cases brought into the Glasgow Casualty units.

During those early training days I had to spend yet another three months away from the Victoria Infirmary to work at the TB hospital in the new town of East Kilbride outside Glasgow. Here patients were in hospital for long stays, from 6 to 12 months, or in some cases longer. It therefore fell upon the nurses and staff who were caring for them to try within their power to make life for the patients as homely and comfortable as possible.

However, as in a lot of cases you can usually find someone who will go the extra mile whether it is right or wrong, and so it was with one nurse who took her night duty too far and was caught one morning in bed with one of her male patients by the day staff that had just come on duty. Professionally, one would be struck off the register for such an act, and so it was in the case of this student nurse who was not allowed to be given any second chance after committing such an unprofessional and immoral deed. To complete her training was out of the question. If a professional was capable of failing in this way it was understandable that one of the routine procedures in that TB hospital included locking the adjoining doors between the male and female inmates, for obvious reasons. After all was said and done, the patients were on the whole physically fit and mobile, but not without their own natural frustrations.

Another of the procedures in the hospital was to count the patients after each visiting hour to ensure no one had left with the visitors. After all, most of the patients did not really feel that ill and were homesick and missed their families, and the temptation of slipping out with them was high. Especially when they had nurses looking after them that would have a go at anything and often at the patients' expense. I have to admit I was guilty of this myself because it was at the TB hospital that I had my first and only attempt at being a hairdresser.

One evening just before visiting time I offered to help a patient look his best by cutting his hair, which was rather long and unkempt, in an attempt to tidy up his appearance to receive his visitors. Unfortunately, I got carried away with enthusiasm and ran the clippers up the back of his head, leaving a perfectly straight bald path up the middle of his skull. I was too much of a coward to admit to him what I had done, so the delighted patient was of course completely unaware of the disastrous haircut that was now on show at the rear of his head as he admired his hairstyle from the front in the mirror. The rest of the patients in the ward, out of loyalty to me, kept quiet about the lawnmower cut – apart from the great hoots of laughter from them whenever the poor trusting victim turned around in bed, obliviously showing them the damage. However, he himself could not fathom out why no more of the male patients wanted me to cut their hair. Well, that was until eventually one of his visitors asked him about his new style and threatened to get the one who did it. Although I thought they were only joking, it was uncanny how I managed to be unavailable on that ward during visiting for some time after that night.

After completing my three-month training at the TB hospital it was time to say my goodbyes to the patients I had got to know so well, and return to work back in the Victoria Infirmary, Glasgow where I was placed on Ward Five under the watchful eye of Sister Shannan.

Now Sister Shannan, a true Highlander, ran her male surgical ward like an army barracks where both staff and patients alike would struggle to attention when she appeared on the ward. One morning while she was giving the ward report to the staff in her usual position at the entrance to the ward, she totally lost her temper, raising the riot act because someone had left the lid off the jam jar in the kitchen when they had been preparing the patients' breakfast. She demanded to know who had been the offender. As the staff looked at each other I trembled in my flat lace-up shoes as I confessed to being the culprit, at the same time wondering what the lid off a jam pot had to do with nursing. Sister Shannan never did explain that to me, but seemed pleased to get the confession.

If Sister Shannan took a dislike to anyone, whether it was a patient or member of staff, like a true Highlander she did not hide the fact from the individual, and if an unfortunate member of the nursing staff was in the firing line they would be given a poor grade as they left the ward to move on to another aspect of their training. Each ward sister that a student nurse worked under graded the nurse A, B, C or D on completion of their time spent on that ward; if the student nurse received a D grade she had to appear before the matron and explain why she had such a low grade. The grades were posted on the main notice-boards for all to see when the change of wards took place, and at the end of training the grades played a major part in the overall exam results alongside the academic written papers.

When Sister Shannan took a dislike to a patient they would be given a smaller portion of food, because she took control of the food trolley when it was wheeled on to the ward at mealtimes and she would serve from it, not allowing the domestic staff to do so.

Should the member of staff out of favour be a consultant she would simply refuse to do the ward round with him and instead send a nurse to chaperone him while he visited his patients.

It was an unwritten rule that there should not be a sound on the ward from the patient or the staff while Mr Gregor the consultant (he was one of Sister Shannan's favoured) did his round. One day when he came on the ward everyone as usual, including the cleaner, scattered at the same time as trying to look busy. But on this particular day Sister Shannan managed to stop the cleaner before she could escape out of sight, to telling her the floor behind the piano at the bottom of the ward needed more polish. Without hesitation the nervous cleaner obeyed and quickly polished up the floor.

At this point I flew into the sluice to sterilise the stainless steel bed pans, but I had not been in there long when a patient requested a bedpan, and being aware that the patient had to be quiet, I quickly carried a pan, which always had to be placed on a tin tray, out into the ward – where I promptly slipped on the newly polished floor. The stainless steel bed pan and tin tray flew in the air, landing on the keys of the piano before clattering to the floor, bringing the ward round to an abrupt halt with everyone staring at me in shock as I tried to look invisible behind the piano. But what was more surprising to everyone than the calamity was the fact that Sister Shannan had been struck dumb, and when she finally did find her voice it was to tell the poor cleaner off and order her to remove the polish applied to the area around the piano. Meanwhile the now desperate patient crossed his legs and waited for calm to be restored before he dared ask again for a bedpan. As for me, I was sure my grades at that point would be the lowest one could expect, but amazingly when I eventually did leave Ward Five I was given a glowing report accompanied by an A grade.

Two years later while I was on night duty on Ward Five there was the death of a rather large gentleman, and while the student nurse and I were preparing the gentleman (washing him and putting on a shroud) I asked the nurse to pull him onto his side facing her while I tied the shroud. This she did, but with the sudden movement of the body the lungs expelled the last of the air in them, which came out making the sound of a groan. At this point the nurse yelled, before taking to her heels and disappearing through the screens, leaving the patient to fall back on top of me. Once I rescued myself from the weight of the deceased man, then settled the disturbed patients that had been awoken with the yell from the panic-stricken nurse, I went in search of the terrified nurse only to find her in the kitchen buttering the bread for the patients' breakfast like mad. However scared she might have been she was conscientious and certainly not afraid of work, nevertheless it was around 2 a.m. – nothing like being early. No doubt she will never forget her experience of dealing with her first death.

Catherine was another of the nurses in the same set as me, in fact she was one of the four who had shared a dorm in the Orthopaedic Hospital at the start of our training. Having had many a conversation during that time we had got to know each other very well, and I knew she had come into nursing to please her father; her own choice would have been to study a career in music. At this point I have to say that although Catherine was academically very bright (first in every exam without any effort of having to study too much) her practical abilities and at times common sense were lacking, mainly because until she had started nursing she had never been expected to do any chores at home, someone else did them for her.

Catherine worked alongside me for a spell on Ward Five and it was here that I witnessed first hand just how unpractical she was. One day she was asked by the staff nurse to go to the kitchen to make an egg sandwich for a patient who had requested one. Catherine dutifully did as she was told and after a time finally produced the request, but unfortunately she omitted to remove the shell from the egg before giving it to the surprised patient. He had removed his false teeth to relieve his tender gums, which were now getting stabbed by pieces of sharp eggshell, as he tried to crunch through his odd sandwich.

There was no doubt that Catherine would have been more at home playing the piano that stood at the bottom of the ward, and probably several of the patients might have preferred that she did. After all was said and done, the piano was never used apart from perhaps the odd Christmas carols sung by the nurses, when they did their annual visit to each ward early on Christmas morning all dressed in their long navy cloaks with the red lining, in an attempt to get the patients into the festive spirit by beginning the day on a note of festive cheer.

6

Believe It

It was during a spell on night duty on Ward Six (the female surgical unit) that I came across a most unusual case, which baffled both the nursing and medical staff at that time.

An elderly lady had been brought in with acute pain in her right foot. This particular night the patient could not settle and even the medication prescribed had no effect in easing her pain. It had turned midnight and having observed how distressed this person was getting, I decided I would have to get to the cause of this pain, so I set to and removed the daily dressing that had been applied to her foot. Once the painful foot had been exposed I was horrified to see that her great toe was being eaten away by maggots. The only way I could describe how it looked was that her toe reminded me of a rotten apple full of holes.

When the night matron Miss Mitchell, a slim, neat, little lady who wore her hair tied up in a bun under her lace cap, came on the ward to do her routine ward round and receive from me the night report, I told her about the maggots. She told me I had been mistaken and in all her years of nursing (which were many) she had never heard of such a thing. Because the painkillers previously given to the patient had at last taken effect, and the patient was now asleep as we stood at the bottom of her bed, I would not disturb her dressing to show the unbelieving Miss Mitchell my findings. After pondering over what I had told her for a few seconds, she dismissed the fact and went on to look at the patient in the next bed before leaving the ward shaking her head, making her lace cap bob up and down as she did so. Nevertheless I was excited about this unusual case and could not wait to give my report to the day sister, who I knew would believe me, but once she had heard it she surprised me by telling me, 'Go to the nurses' home and get some much-needed sleep.'

When I returned that evening to start my shift the nursing staff on duty that day was buzzing with interest at such an unusual case. The unfortunate patient had been taken to theatre that day where her right leg had been amputated above the knee. The history was that the lady lived on a farm and during one of her many walks through the fields when she had been wearing open-toed sandals she had at some stage cut her great toe, and the eggs from maggots from sheep droppings had got into the wound, later hatching and causing the problem that resulted in the poor lady losing her leg. That same evening when Miss Mitchell did her ward round she had to admit she was never too old to learn. As for me, I have never looked at a bad apple since without thinking of that little lady on Ward Six.

Night duty on Ward Six was always unpredictable, mainly because some of the elderly patients, especially those who were suffering from fractures, would frequently become confused when nightfall came. This was partly due to the pain they endured and partly because of the effect the analgesics given for the pain had on them but mainly because they were away from home and their own environment.

'Catch that cat,' called one old lady as I walked on to the ward.

In an attempt to pacify her I ran down the ward and picked up an imaginary cat and pretending to stroke, it carried it back to her bed.

'Here is your cat, now you can settle,' I smiled.

'I knew it,' she said. 'It's not me that's daft; it's you that's daft. There is no cat.'

The fun of the night had begun two beds down. Peggy was calling me: 'Nurse, put the milk bottles out.'

Here again I went through the motions, pretending to put out the milk bottles.

'That's better,' was her reply.

'Now wind the clock up.'

After a busy but amazing night I started the morning duties by doing the ward round, distributing the patients' medication. I stopped at the foot of Alice's bed and was studying the drug list when Alice sat up in her cot-sided bed in an agitated state. First she wanted my pen, then she wanted my watch, before moving on to wanting the trolley and its contents. So in exasperation, in an attempt to keep her quiet while I concentrated on my duties, I gave her the nearest, safest thing I had to hand, which happened to be a crepe bandage, for her to fiddle with.

This bandage kept Alice quiet for a few minutes before she called again. I looked up from my trolley to find her handing me back my bandage, but the bandage was now covered in porridge where she had tried to wrap up her breakfast. This was her way of giving me my take-away breakfast as I came off duty, her way of building me up ready for the following night and what it might have in store.

Working in a hospital in the city always had its nights of drama in some form or another. One night a young man was admitted to the medical ward I was on, accompanied by the police. The young man's condition on admission was fairly serious and the fact that his injuries were severe meant that he would be under special observation throughout the night by the medical staff. In the event that he might be able to clarify how he had sustained the injuries, the police sat by his bedside.

The story was that his parents had gone out for the evening leaving their teenaged son (the patient) and his teenaged sister at home. When the ambulance had been called to the home (which was one of the large tenement buildings in Glasgow) the distressed sister told them someone had knocked on their door and when her brother had answered it the caller had attacked him with a hammer, hitting him over the head. Hearing the thud she had found her brother slumped unconscious in a heap by the front door in a pool of blood, but there was no sign of the offender.

The police were not convinced that they had been given the full story and after interviewing the sister for some time discovered the truth, which was that the brother and sister had had a domestic argument and in the heat of the moment, the sister had lost her temper and had struck her brother using a hammer. Her dad had left it lying around after he had finished a job, and because he and his wife were in a hurry to get to their engagement that evening had not put it back in the tool box under the stairs. Thankfully the young man did survive and the sister was charged, but the family understandably were never the same again. This was my first encounter with such a violent case, and what seemed more of a shock was that the unexpected can happen to anyone; such physical damage had been inflicted from within what had appeared to be quite a respectable family living in such a nice area of Glasgow.

Thankfully the outcomes of cases were not all dreadful. One of the amazing recoveries occurred when I was working on the burns unit in the Infirmary, and a man was brought in who had been badly injured in an explosion that happened in the foundry he was working at in Glasgow. When the man was admitted to the ward his face was burnt black, and most of his body had received second degree burns. After a few days he would sit up in bed, looking like a burnt-out matchstick, and when ever anyone entered the ward they could smell his burnt skin. But by the time the man was ready to be discharged home which was several weeks after his admission, the skin on his face was as new as a baby's with no visible scars seen, a credit to the skills administered by the medical staff who cared for him.

The burns patient was not the only one to be leaving the Victoria Hospital after his long stay: a few of the nurses were anticipating a final move also. When the final nursing examination results were displayed on the noticeboard in the corridor outside the nurses' sitting room at the Victoria Hospital, the third-year nurses including myself gathered around it in anticipation, to scan the list for our names and, more important, the word 'Pass' or 'Fail'. After finding our own results we then searched for the names of our friends and colleagues and their results, after which the squeals of delight could be heard along the main corridor leading to the wards, and also the patients bedded in the first ward could hear. Some of the patients already knew the results were due out and were keen to find out if the nurses on their ward had passed.

After checking and rechecking the list we, the final-year nurses, made our way down to the basement to the post room where we collected our written result, handed over to us in a sealed envelope once they had been signed for. Once each of us had absorbed each individual subject results such as anatomy, physiology, surgery, medicine and nursing care, and having grasped the fact that we had now completed our general nursing student days and crossed the line to become staff nurses, we made a bee-line to queue for the phone to contact our families to share with them our joy of passing our finals.

Now the reality of passing our exams had sunk in it, was time for important decisions to be made about the future; some nurses they would move to other hospitals nearer their homes, some moved into further training in different disciples of nursing, while others like myself chose to take up the position of staff nurse within our own hospital to enable us to gain experience and knowledge and at the same time to act as a mentors to the new student nurses under instruction on the wards that we were now in charge of.

I was fortunate to be given the post of staff nurse for the surgical theatre, an aspect of nursing that I really enjoyed, and that I found to be – believe it or not – one of the most relaxed areas within the hospital. Most of the surgeons I had the pleasure to work with proved to be totally different characters once they had changed into their green gowns, and, scrubbed up ready to apply their many surgical skills to improve the lives of the patients that came under their scalpels.

The atmosphere in theatre was usually always relaxed: some of the surgeons enjoyed listening to the sound of background music while they worked down their theatre list; others chatted freely about anything but work, sharing humour with their assisting staff – this helped to relieve them of any would-be tensions they might be concealing. On one such occasion an eminent surgeon asked affectionately if the theatre porters would 'Get the old duck on the table?'

We learned later that the patient, who was not fully anaesthetised (which was often the case until they reached the table), had heard everything and once she was back on the ward had complained at being called an 'old duck'. Sadly the complaint against such a caring surgeon was unfortunate, because if the patient had known the doctor as the staff did, she would never have reported him. The fact that the operation had been carried out with the utmost care, and that the patient had been left with a neat surgical scar that would fade with time, and that she made a swift and complete recovery, altered her first reactions, causing her to retract her complaint. However, this still left the surgeon to reflect on the upset he had caused her, and for some time after that incident he remained quiet while performing his skills.

Although to some, surgery might seem a bit gruesome, I never found it to be so – apart from the time when I was observing an orthopaedic operation where the unfortunate patient had been brought in for a leg amputation. It was the noise of the limb being sawn off that was unforgettable and made the hairs on the back of my neck stand up on end, and the speed at which the severed limb was instantly removed from the scene, taken away by a hospital attendant who was standing by with a surgical waste bag to collect the limb to disposed of in the hospital incinerator.

Another upsetting operation I had the misfortune to witness while I assisted in the gynaecological theatre was that of a young lady brought in for a termination of her pregnancy. It was after the procedure had been carried out that I was handed the kidney dish containing the tiny foetus that had been removed from the womb, for me to take into the sluice. I could only feel a deep sadness as I studied this little being that was fully formed but nevertheless for some reason unwanted. The making of this decision by this young mother could not have been easy, and certainly one that not any person had the right to judge. However, such surgery always had an effect on the theatre staff present at the time of such an operation.

Having completed a few months of surgical experience it was now time for me to move on to another aspect of nursing, and since Margaret, Bill and the twins had recently moved to Shropshire to live, to be near Bill's dad who lived in Ironbridge and was very ill at the time, I decided that England was where I would like to start my midwifery training.

It was 10 p.m. when I stepped on the overnight bus that was to take me to my new home in Shropshire, England. Two of my nursing friends, Aileen and Nessy, had travelled with me across Glasgow from the nurses' home at the Victoria Infirmary to wave me off. We had passed our finals and were newly qualified as State Registered Nurses (SRN), after sharing three years of studying, swotting, and sharing tears and laughter. Like the few times when the sun did shine in Glasgow and we would grasp the opportunity while off duty to catch its hot rays, by rushing onto the flat roof of the nurses' home and stripping off to our pants and bra. We would cover ourselves in a mixture of olive oil and vinegar before lying on a towel on the hard surface of the bitumen roofing to cook in the sun.

After an hour or so (depending how long the sun was out) we would return to our rooms to prepare for duty. Aileen, tall and slim, would arrive on the ward displaying a deep tan, while Nessy, tall and attractive, would have a glowing golden tan. As for me, well I never did tan easily so I would be burnt bright red, covered in freckles, and still smelling like a bag of chips despite the painful shower to remove the makeshift sun tan lotion.

Now we were preparing to go our separate ways in our nursing career. It had been only a few weeks earlier we had tried to forecast what our future would be as we walked along the beach at Gourock one weekend when we had the same days off. Aileen had suggested that I would end up married with lots of children and give up my nursing career to be a full-time wife and mother.

She had also predicted that Nessy would marry Gordon (her current boyfriend) and have two children, while continuing with her nursing career. We on the other hand predicted that Aileen might marry after reaching her peak in her nursing profession, and have one child.

How wrong could we all have been? Although we all did marry, the predictions were completely off key. Nessy did marry her Gordon and had four boys, and three of them married Irish girls, giving Nessy and Gordon many lovely grandchildren: their youngest son completed his studies at university and bought a house in London. Nessy, who had been a first-class student during her nursing training, had given up her nursing to raise her family and be a good wife to her husband who was the headmaster at a school in Fife; however she sadly lost Gordon, who died at an early age.

Aileen married soon after qualifying, and over the years had three children. She also moved on from doing general nursing to do her Part 1 midwifery training before eventually running an old folks' home in Scotland. As for me, after moving to England to complete my midwifery training it was during the interval between Part 1 midwifery and Part 2 that I met Keith (my driving instructor), whom I later married, and five years later we had Craig. I was to go on nursing until my retirement.

The bus left Buchanan Street, taking me away from working in Glasgow for the last time. As I waved farewell to my dear friends to head for England, where the people speak differently, I felt nervous but excited and I looked forward to being near Margaret, Bill and the twins again and starting my midwifery training. Having watched my friends until they faded from view in the darkness, I settled down in my seat and, after what had been a tiring day, soon slept to dream of the future.

Once the bus had crossed over the Scottish borders it made its way through the English countryside. As day broke the sight of the bare brick houses in England made me wonder whether they were unfinished, or if the builder had just run out of money and had been unable to render them. I was puzzled because most of the houses in Scotland at that time were either stucco (rendered) or Victorian stone finished.

After many hours the bus came to a holt in Hood Street in Minton. Here I descended, tired and weary but ready to start my new life in this new country. The warm welcome I received from the family and the excitement of the twins reassured me that I was doing the right thing in coming to continue my nursing career in England – after all, it had been a big step to take, leaving my beloved Scotland.

7

Starting Afresh

There was a gap of two months before I was due to start my Part 1 midwifery training, so six weeks of this was taken up with me working for a private nursing agency in London. My illusion of getting rich quick in private nursing was to be dashed as I discovered 12 per cent of my salary went to the agency, and the remainder was soon swallowed up with the high cost of living in London. But thankfully for me as my sister Nancy and her family lived and worked in London, my accommodation was already available. This proved to be of great advantage: not only had I a loving family to stay with, but also I had an elder sister to guide me as to the 'Dangers of London'. After all I was a lass just up from the country. The time I spent with my big sister and her family was a period to treasure because Nancy had left Scotland when I was quite young, and this gave us the opportunity to catch up and get to know each other's sense of humour, which we shared frequently in the six weeks I was there.

Life in London during that time was hectic. The agency I was working for placed me in a large old hospital in Ladywell near Blackheath; the ward I was in charge of had 60 patients, dividing the male and female patients by a small corridor that had a few single rooms on each side of it. Many of the patients were terminally ill and most of them were 'heavy nursing'. The majority of the staff working on the ward were auxilliaries, most of which were coloured girls, London being multicultural. Although this was not uncommon in the capital it was quite new to me but something I adjusted to quickly. There were very few trained staff in the hospital (perhaps because management ran it on a budget, plus the fact it was not a training hospital), therefore part of my work was to do a hospital ward round on the evenings I was on duty.

It was during these ward rounds that I met some nurses who were from Ireland, who after a heavy day at work were always ready to let their hair down in the form of a party. They shared an upper-floor flat and below them were a crowd of male university students who also shared accommodation, so between the two there was never any shortage of parties to go to.

One evening I set off to one of these lively parties feeling like the bee's knees. I was wearing a lovely multicoloured dress Nancy had just made (she has always been a dab hand on the sewing machine) and was accompanied by a male friend as we arrived at the party. Some hours later a very nice young man approached me and asked if he could take me home. I agreed, and we set off down the stairs of the flat. Midway down he turned to me and asked me if I would wait while he ran back upstairs to get his car keys, which he had forgotten. I sat on the step in the dark and waited. A few minutes later he came running down the stairs and fell over me in the dark, kicking me in the head as he landed in a heap through the open front door. He felt no pain, or so he said as he quickly scrambled to his feet to check if I was OK; I was too embarrassed to complain that my kicked-in head was only hanging on by my neck, so I smiled and said, 'I'm OK.'

This was the start of an ongoing friendship; later when I left the lights of London to move to the Sorrento Maternity Hospital in Birmingham where I was to spend my first six months' training to become a midwife, my new friend (now a student at Coventry University) became a regular visitor to the doors of the nurses' home to pick me up, under the watchful eyes of my nursing colleagues as they peeped at him behind the curtains in the nurses' day room.

It was while I was at the Sorrento that I got to know Jean, also a student midwife. We shared a very large room in the nurses' home at the same time as sharing a great deal of laughter. Jean was from Stoke-on-Trent and her accent used to amuse me no end, especially her use of the word 'Duck' that she affectionately added to each sentence whoever she was speaking to. I will always remember Jean for her constant baths: she would spend hours in the water, it was her way of relaxing, and I am sure it was where she found it easier to gather her thoughts together after we had shared a heavy session of hours of studying for our exams.

At the completion of our Part 1 midwifery training it was time to say our goodbyes. Jean was going back home to Stoke-on-Trent to complete her midwifery training where later she married Stuart, who in years gone by had been the boy next door, and later they had three lovely children. I was moving back to Shropshire to commence my Part 2 training at Copthorne Hospital in Shrewsbury.

Once again there was a period of time between finishing one lot of training and starting another, so I filled this gap by nursing in the geriatric unit at the Tinto Hospital in Minton where I met for the first time a colourful character: of Miss Conney, the matron. One of my first encounters with this little Irish lady was when she interviewed me shortly after I had started on C Block, the male geriatric unit. I had to go to her office one day to request some equipment I needed on the ward and as we were allowed an annual budget for the year, all requests had to be approved by Matron, who took pride in keeping to her given budget. During this visit the conversation went something like this:

'Ah! Sister Dickie, now I have you here tell me,' she demanded, 'Are you married?'

'No,' I replied.

'Well, are you engaged?'

'No.'

'Have you got a boyfriend?'

'Yes.'

'Well I don't want you coming here telling me you're pregnant,' she ordered.

'And what business would that be of yours, Miss Conney?' I firmly replied.

I turned on my heels, heading back to the ward, leaving the stern little woman open-mouthed and speechless sitting in her wee chair behind an over-large desk.

From that day forward Matron and I got on fine. It takes a Celt to know a Celt. She never did turn down any request made for the benefit of the patients on my ward, one of which was to allow some of the old gentlemen to have a small bottle of shandy occasionally of an evening; especially George, an old character who had been on the ward for a long time. He had served his younger days in the Army and had reached the rank of sergeant before retiring.

Now George was a proper gentleman in his day but old age had taken its toll and left him a little senile and confused, but with a large appetite that never seemed to be satisfied: so much so that George would often go on the wander and raid the other patients' lockers of any edibles their visitors had brought them.

One evening after I had gone off duty George was found walking along the Lincon Road in Minton wearing only his pyjama top, unaware of his nudity on his search for food. When I returned on duty the following day George was back on the prowl, stealing what he could find. He was completely oblivious to his adventures the day before or the commotion he had caused among the public as they drove past on their way to Shrewsbury. He had been reported to the police, who had rescued him and brought him back to the Tinto Hospital.

Some months later I had to leave George and the rest of the elderly in C Block to move on to help in the delivery of the newborn babies over at Copthorne Maternity Hospital in Shrewsbury.

One day while I was in the district doing my rounds as a pupil midwife, there had been a heavy snowfall the night before and all the byroads had not been cleared, making access difficult to my patients' homes, especially around the estates. I was visiting one of my ladies on an estate in Shrewsbury and had to park in the middle of the road because the snow was so deep by the kerb. After about half an hour when I had examined my lady-in-waiting, we were enjoying a cup of tea when her doorbell rang vigorously. The lady of the house opened the door to her neighbour, who stood there out of breath.

'Can you tell the midwife the bus can't get past her car and the driver is not very happy about it.'

Hearing this I put on a face mask and hurried down to the bus which was full of passengers and the red-faced driver who was now puffing hot air from his ears.

'Sorry,' I said. And before he could answer, I added, 'You just can't keep the baby waiting.'

Hearing this the red-faced driver sat upright and smiled, 'Oh! Don't worry, it's OK.'

At this statement, I jumped in my car and drove out of sight, heaving a sigh of relief.

During the period of time I spent doing my home deliveries in the Shrewsbury area, the various antenatal ladies I nursed varied from working class to those who had plenty, quite a contrast to some of the postnatal ladies I had visited in the past, back in my days in Birmingham. There the maternity unit would pay them two pennies a fluid ounce for any excess breast milk they had expressed off, in an attempt to help supply the premature babies whose mothers were unable to breastfeed them in the baby unit at the Sorrento.

As in all things in life, some things touch us more than others. So it was with one home delivery I attended in Shrewsbury where the family went to borrow a chair from a neighbour, so that I had something to place my delivery bag on to enable me to get easy access to the instruments I needed during the delivery of the baby. This same family was a very loving family who were always willing to share with me what little they had whenever I visited my patient; even though they did not own a teacup that still had a handle on it they always offered me a cup of tea. For me that tea in the chipped cup was extra special, knowing how lovingly it had been made.

That same week I visited an antenatal lady living in another area of the town. This lady and her husband owned a grand house which had an impressive staircase that led to a balcony surrounding the upper floor with the bedrooms leading off from it. The mother-to-be (who was due to deliver any day soon) led me into her beautiful bedroom, fitted with a white carpet, the sight of which left me wondering how I would protect that spotless carpet I was standing on, dreading the thought of any staining that could occur during her delivery.

As things turned out there was no need for me to be anxious: the delivery went without a hitch with the carpet maintaining its former glory. I visited the home the following morning after the lady had delivered her baby boy to do my routine check on mother and baby, and as I entered the house through the kitchen I was aware of how the other half live: the work top was covered with silver ice buckets each containing several empty champagne bottles, just some of the evidence left over from the celebrations that had taken place the previous night. Such a contrast from the home I had attended earlier in the week.

Nevertheless, comparing the differences between the two homes, I knew which home I felt more at ease in. However, there are no differences to compare when a baby is born because every baby delivered is still a miracle, and each one as pretty as the next.

One of the most wonderful deliveries I performed as a midwife was when I delivered my sister Helen's baby, Shona. It was Sunday 21st January 1968 and I was spending my day off at Keith's parents' home with his mum and dad – soon to become my in-laws – along with my future sister-in-law Ann. Keith was working as a driving instructor with his own school of motoring: he was putting in some long hours in preparation for our coming wedding.

I had asked the staff on duty on the labour ward at the Shrewsbury maternity unit (a renamed new unit built opposite the old) to keep me informed as to Helen's progress in labour, so that I could assess how long it would take me to get from Jackend to Shrewsbury, some 16 miles away. This was a delivery I did not want to miss.

Throughout the afternoon I had several phone calls from the maternity unit, keeping me informed about Helen and her stages of labour, before I had the ultimate call: 'You had better get here if you want to deliver this baby.'

I jumped up after bidding my farewells and dashed through the door of Keith's family home, only to come to an abrupt halt as I found my car was blocked in their drive by Ann's car parked behind it. Rushing back indoors, I asked her if she could move her car.

'I'll take you to Shrewsbury,' Ann said.

'Oh I don't know,' I muttered.

'It will be quicker than moving cars.'

I agreed, anything to get there quickly, and so we set off. It was a lovely sunny afternoon for January and it appeared to have brought out most of Rosebank's population plus the Sunday drivers intending to make the most of the weather. This extra traffic seemed to make our journey slower than normal, not helped by the fact that we were travelling along the A5 stuck behind a lorry. After a few miles, and feeling a little anxious, I asked, 'Ann, could you overtake that lorry'

'Why, what's the hurry?' she queried.

'Well, I do want to deliver Helen's baby,' I replied, puzzled that she should ask.

'Oh! I thought you were just going to see her.'

For the remainder of the journey the car wheels burned rubber until we arrived at the hospital where I abandoned Ann and ran to the ward. As I reached the labour unit a student midwife was waiting to help me into a sterile gown and gloves. Once adorned I rushed into the room where Helen was struggling to hold on to a baby that was in a hurry to be born, until I arrived.

'I think I am going to scream,' were her first words to me.

'Oh no you're not,' I warned as I opened the delivery pack. And within minutes I had the thrill of delivering my niece, who to my great relief (after an examination of her) was a lovely perfect baby. And as for Helen, well, she never did scream, she was too busy pushing. After all this was her fourth, and last, baby.

Ladies in labour can do strange and sometimes unexpected things. I was with one patient who had been struggling with discomfort in a long labour when, feeling she had had enough, she took off her wedding ring and threw it at the door of the labour room as she lay blaming her absent husband. I did wonder what she might have done to her husband had he been there at the time. However all was soon forgotten and forgiven when she was delivered of a healthy beautiful baby and her husband arrived, beaming from ear to ear.

Another delivery I will not forget was one that happened while I was on the district as a student midwife, doing my home visits to ladies who were booked to have their babies at home. I had been called to one of my antenatal ladies who had started in the first stage of labour. After I had palpated the lady and had a listen to the baby, I thought I could hear not one but two heartbeats. Listening again I was convinced this was an undiagnosed twin pregnancy, in which case it should not be a home delivery but a hospital delivery under the supervision of a consultant, in case of any complications that might occur.

Taking the bull by the horns I did not hesitate to phone the maternity unit to express my concern, thinking I would rather be proved wrong than be left alone to deliver twins. To my relief and surprise within 15 minutes Mr Blake, the consultant, arrived at the house. The sight of such a great man coming out of hospital on my say-so made me more than a little nervous that I might be wasting his time. Mr Blake soon put me at ease with his smile as he asked me to take him to the patient, where he quickly confirmed that the lady was carrying twins. After his examination of the lady he went downstairs to reassure her husband and keep him company, leaving me upstairs to stay with the patient until delivery was imminent. By now I was completely at ease, knowing he was there for the birth. Then Mr Blake came back upstairs and delivered twin boys to the delighted parents, who were still in shock at having two babies instead of one.

In those days, because it was standard procedure in many cases for ladies to request a home delivery, the maternity unit provided an emergency cover team. This team, called the Flying Squad, was led by a consultant or a doctor accompanied by midwives. The team would be on call in the event of a patient needing a blood transfusion after a difficult birth, or another such emergency occurring prior to getting the patient to hospital.

One night around midnight Mr Clarke, a consultant, was on his way to a call from the Flying Squad. He was driving along a country road past a woodland on his way to a remote farm house when suddenly, out of the dark, a police car with two officers in it stopped him.

'Where are you going?' asked the officer

Mr Clarke hurriedly explained his mission and who he was, anxious to get to the patient who needed help.

'Sorry sir, we will have to check your boot,' insisted the officer.

'I really am in a hurry,' explained Mr Clarke.

'We will still have to check,' said the officer.

The consultant clicked the switch to open the boot of the car and the officer, seeing the medical equipment, closed the boot and walked to the driver's window.

'Sorry sir, but there has been a lot of Christmas trees stolen in this area, and we just had to make sure you did not have one in your boot,' smiled the officer.

'What! Carry a Christmas tree in my Bentley?' said the consultant as he drove away.

8

Black Bess

The lights had just changed to red as I approached the railway station in Shrewsbury, then after a few minutes, to my shock, the car would not go into first gear when I tried to move on the green light. A convoy of buses and cars were mounting up behind me as I watched the lights go back to red for the third time; I just sat there at a loss not knowing what to do. It was 8 a.m. and I was on my way to work at the Maternity Hospital the other side of town.

While I struggled for the umpteenth time to get the car into gear, I suddenly felt the car move slowly and steadily. I turned round to see what had happened, and there to my surprise were the passengers from the bus, pushing my car out of the way into the railway station car park – the first left turning after the traffic lights. The men on the bus were anxious to get to work and decided they could not wait any longer, so I was pushed into a prohibited car space (it was the nearest there was).

Once I was left there I was too relieved to be embarrassed and I phoned the police to tell them what had happened, asking them to keep an eye on my car until I came off duty when I could get someone to fix it. Within minutes a police car with two officers arrived at the station to checkout this car that was my pride and joy. To their amusement they were expected to guard an old banger, a black Hillman Minx that looked like a hearse, although it did have real leather seats which I was very proud to be the owner of.

The police officers kindly assured me it would be OK until I

76

came off duty, and then they drove me through town and dropped me at the hospital, much to the amazement of my colleagues who were watching from the ward window as the two handsome officers opened the door of the police car for me. As expected, the word soon got around the staff canteen and I spent the rest of the day explaining my arrest to whoever asked. During my lunch break I contacted my brother-in-law Bill and told him my problem. To my delight he with his friend Jim, who had a van with a tow bar, was waiting for me as I came off duty. Bill, who was an electrician, had been rewiring Jim's house in Bridgenorth when I rang, and Jim had kindly offered to tow my car back home.

So off the three of us went in Jim's old blue van to pick up Black Bess, as I called my car. Once at the railway station Bill got in my car while Jim and I got in the van and towed Bill through the town, then on to the back road to Bridgenorth. As I sat in the front of the van Jim started to swerve from side to side along the country lanes: he was driving with one hand while with his other he was trying to grab something on his windscreen. In the meantime Bill was getting thrown all over the road as the van zigzagged along.

'What are you doing, Jim?' I asked.

'Trying to catch that fly,' he grinned.

'You drive, and I'll catch the fly.'

I started diving all over the bench seat in vain after a fly that was determined not to be caught. Finally, after what seemed like an age, we three arrived safely back home.

A few days later I heard that Jim had come home from work unexpectedly and found his wife in bed with someone else, the outcome of which resulted in their marriage coming to an end. Jim, when reluctantly giving his wife her share of the contents of the house as they parted, had taken an axe to the bed and halved it. Fortunately she was not in it at the time. Thankfully I never needed to ask for Jim's help again.

After the problem with my car I decided I should do something about getting a more reliable vehicle, so one morning on my way home from night duty I called into Lloyds Bank and requested to see the bank manager. I was soon shown into his office, where the friendly bank manager asked how he could be of help to me. I sat exhausted after my eight hours on night duty in one of his comfortable large leather chairs, and asked him if I could have some money to buy a car.

'Have you got any collateral, a house, or savings?' he enquired.

'No, but I do need a car to get back and forth to work,' I said.

'I'll tell you what you should do, go home and have a well-earned sleep and think about it.'

Smiling, he got up out of his wing desk chair and, coming around to my chair, took my arm and helped me to my feet, then he ushered me out his door.

I never did have a loan, but somehow the bank manager ended up buying my Black Bess for his son for the grand total of £5, and for some time later it was seen being driven around the area, easily noticeable by its black gleaming appearance, complemented by the red leather seats and looking in mint condition.

It was while I was on night duty on maternity at the Royal Shrewsbury Hospital that I got to know Jo; she was an auxiliary working on the same ward, where we shared the same sense of humour. As Jo lived in Erton (on my way home) I was able to offer her a lift to and from work, and during the journey home we were able to talk over the night's events and laugh a lot at the antics of some of the folk we worked alongside.

One morning on our way home after a busy night I waited at a road junction to give way to a car. This gesture ended with me allowing a convoy of cars out behind it. It turned out to be a funeral party which we had no option but to follow.

'Why don't you overtake them?' asked Jo.

'I have always been told it is not respectful to overtake a funeral car.'

'OK, so they think we are part of the funeral party,' Jo grinned.

We drove the rest of the journey in second gear and laughed with tiredness all the way home.

On another journey home one morning, Jo asked me if I would stop at a lay-by in the country lane, so that she could dispose of an unwanted gift that a fellow worker had given her as she came off duty.

'But why would you want to throw away a present?' I asked.

'I'll show you,' she said.

Once I had found the appropriate spot, which was quiet and happened to be a lay-by at the side of a field, I stopped the car and Jo took an old bashed cardboard box from the boot where she had placed it before leaving the hospital. She opened the box and showed me an electric blanket.

'Well, what's wrong with that?' I queried.

She opened the blanket up to display a large stain in the middle. 'It's been weed on,' she said, screwing up her face.

She took a quick look around to make sure no one was watching, especially the farmer of the field it was going in, then being satisfied that there was no witness to her fly-tipping she threw it over the hedge.

Needless to say we were sore from laughing by the time we got home, although I doubt that the farmer would be laughing when he came across not only an old box but also a smelly old blanket in it, and not even one he could use for his dogs to sleep on.

Some years later I met Jo while she was doing her shopping in the Co-op in Bendigo. She was waiting in the queue at the checkout in front of me, and the conversation went like this.

'How are you? You look great,' said Jo when she saw me coming towards her.

'Oh I am fine thank you.'

'I have just been to the hospital where they passed a tube down my throat to have a look at my bladder.' She demonstrated the action.

Her bladder must have moved, I thought.

'How is Ian?' she asked.

'Well, he is alright, except his name is Keith,' I smiled.

'No not your husband,' she laughed, 'your son.'

'He is OK too, but his name is Craig.'

'Oh you haven't changed, you get no better. I can't believe you have forgotten him,' she grinned.

'You'd better get in line or you will miss your turn.'

I made my escape, still wondering who Ian was.

Although Jo and I shared our journey from Shrewsbury, as a midwife some of my time would be spent working in Shrewsbury for several months and some time would be spent in the unit at Minton, depending on the staff coverage and where we were needed. As a midwife I did not really have a say in where I preferred to work or where might be more convenient regarding location and travel: however I did like working in Minton where I found it to be more personal with less complicated deliveries for the patients. And because it was a smaller unit with their own GPs in attendance at the delivery, a familiar face helped the mothers to enjoy the experience of having their baby, especially if it was their first. Complicated pregnancies were automatically booked to deliver at Shrewsbury in the consultant unit, and although as a midwife one could gain a lot of experience and at the same time it could prove to be more interesting, it was also more clinical and less personal for the mothers because it was such a busy unit with a lot of turnover, having ladies from as far as Wales booked for their delivery.

With less complicated deliveries it was a more relaxed unit and at times there was more freedom for the staff, with the absence of consultants floating around requiring attention. While I was a sister on the maternity unit at the Tinto Hospital in Minton, often the vein of humour would run through the staff, and they would be up to some trick or other when ever they got the chance or the time. One afternoon while I was sitting in the office trying to catch up with my paperwork, two of the staff rushed down the corridor pushing a very pregnant lady on a trolley. There was a loud moaning coming from the patient who was covered over except for her long hair hanging over the top of the trolley.

'Sister come quickly,' called the staff as they passed my door.

'How far advanced is she?' I asked getting up from my desk and following behind them into the delivery room.

'Nearly ready to push.'

'I didn't know we were expecting a new admission.'

I had now reached the patient and was removing the sheet from her face. As I did so, to my surprise and the amusement of the staff, the patient stopped moaning and sat upright on the trolley only to reveal that instead of a lady in labour, it was one of the porters wearing a very long wig. This was his way of getting his own back on me for all the tricks I had played on him in the past.

On my last afternoon at the Tinto maternity unit before leaving to get married and take up my new post as a practice nurse at a local GP surgery, the staff burst into the office where I was once again trying to complete my paperwork, and grabbing me two of the porters held me while some of the nurses poured rice grains down my neck before they sprayed me with water, causing the rice to swell under my uniform. Now I knew what it felt like to be a pot of rice pudding. After a few hours of putting up with their antics it was time to say my goodbyes to a jolly staff I had enjoyed working with for several months. I left the ward still all sticky because my colleagues would not allow me to change out of my uniform before going home, and as I turned the corner to the car park I found my car covered in balloons with slogans written in foam all over the windows, leaving me no option but to drive home from Minton to Grampion (where I lived with Margaret and Bill) advertising to all on the way that I was about to get married.

From that day on the time just seemed to fly: the days were filled with dashing here and there making the final arrangements for the wedding, and planning the guest list of who was coming and where they would be staying. Then before I knew it the 9th of August had come and gone and two weeks ago had been my wedding to Keith. Strange, some would say, marrying your driving instructor, but then right from the first lesson there had been a spark between us and it had not come from the spark plugs. We got on well, probably because I never stopped talking while having my driving lesson mainly due to nerves at being in control of an engine, leaving Keith unable to get a word in apart from the odd instruction such as 'Stop!' At the same time as trying to understand my Scottish tongue.

Often when we were courting, Keith would drive to Shrewsbury after teaching his last pupil of the day to see me at the nursing home at Copthorne Hospital where I was on call as a midwife. Because I was unable to leave the hospital premises in case one of my antenatal ladies decided to go into labour, he would park in the only place he could, which was outside the morgue and I would join him knowing I was within reach of being called to the phone should it be necessary. One evening at around 11 p.m. I decided he must be serious about our relationship when he offered me one of his polony sandwiches: this was part of his packed lunch which he was unable to devour in the day due to his full appointment diary. Who says romance is dead? The truth was that he had not eaten since breakfast and was too hungry to wait any longer, although I never did like polony.

The wedding had been an event in itself, starting from the Friday evening before the big day on 9th August 1969, when I set off with Bill slowly driving through the cobbled streets of Riverdale with me balancing the three-tiered cake that my sister Margaret had so lovingly baked and decorated to perfection. I felt so relieved as the work of art with all its delicate lace work made out of icing reached the Vine Hotel intact. As to be expected, the wedding day had not gone without its hiccups, and there was the usual household panic that most brides experience prior to the car arriving to take them to their fate.

In my case it started with a call of distress from Aunt Jessie who had arrived from Scotland the night before and had wasted no time in getting into mischief, by placing thistles (which she had brought with her) in the bottom of Bill's bed between the sheets as a wake-up call for him before the start of the big day. She was now busy, on the morning of the wedding, getting dressed when she discovered she had not got a pin to anchor her flower to her not-so-generous bosom, while her sister Aunt Agnes who had travelled with her from Scotland had just lost her suspender button. So Susan, my adorable niece and now a delighted brides-maid, improvised and solved Aunt Agnes's problem with a Polo mint which she had sucked to the right size to hold the suspender in place, or at least until the sticky mint dried and broke and Aunt Agnes used a button instead.

Then there was the arrival at the church, when Bill my hand-some 6 foot 2 brother-in-law, who had the honour of giving me away, stood on my flowing veil with his size twelves and nearly tugged the ornate headpiece from my carefully arranged hairdo as we got out of the wedding car. Just the sort of thing a bride wants before entering a full church of waiting guests, some of which I had not seen for years.

The reception also proved to be a topic of amusing conversa-tion in the years that followed although at the time it seemed to be a disaster and an embarrassment. Aunt Agnes sat at her table behind a pile of dirty dinner plates which she had collected from everyone surrounding her, as a kind gesture to help the waitress. At the same time she carried on a conversation in her broad Scot-tish accent, addressing a bewildered English guest across the table who could only see Aunt Agnes's hands from behind the moun-tain of dirty crocks, and was no doubt relieved that she did not have to look into the face of Aunt Agnes because she could not understanding a word.

At the other end of the table cousin Eleanor, feeling rather hot removed her hat. Unfortunately the wig she was wearing under it came off too, and was still inside the hat, leaving Eleanor happily sitting, totally unaware of how she looked with her own wet hair stuck to her head in a tousled manner. All this had been witnessed by two of my new bosses, Dr Munro and Dr Turnball, who to my delight had found time in their busy schedule to attend.

After the wedding reception Keith and I left the guests enjoying the evening party, which continued late into the wee small hours before most of them finally ended up at Margaret and Bill's home in Grampion. By which time we were well on our way, heading for two weeks' honeymoon in Newquay, Cornwall, where during the first week both Keith and I suffered sunstroke after falling asleep on the beach. This resulted in me having to spend a day of my honeymoon in bed, suffering the effects caused by the hot sun much to the embarrassment of my new husband who was trying to hide the fact that we were newly-weds and pretend to the other guests at the hotel that we were old hands at this married lark.

Not that anyone was fooled by him, because on the second evening while talking to the proprietors of the hotel he tried to disguise the fact that we were on honeymoon by chatting as though we had been married for years, only to be caught out by them when they asked about our garden and what was planted in it. These questions completely baffled Keith who, up until getting married, had left all the gardening to his dad; and the smile on the hotel owners' faces showed they knew the truth.

Now back home with the honeymoon over, and as a new wife, I was ready to start my new life in a new discipline of my nursing career at the Boweryhill Surgery in Bendigo. As I entered the doors of the brand new practice and approached the reception window I was greeted with the receptionist in her Cockney accent asking, 'What's your name? Do you have an appointment?'

She was 5' 8" tall with short blonde hair, and very confident, having an air of authority. As she picked up her pen to tick me in, the ring finger on her right hand displayed a ring mounted with a clear stone that Liz Taylor could have owned had it been authentic.

'Lynn Smart. I am the new practice nurse,' I replied.

I was wondering what I had let myself in for, despite the fact that I had been headhunted by the two rival groups of doctors who were both setting up their new general practices at opposite ends of the town in Bendigo: which would no doubt prove to be a great asset to the people who lived there, after all the town was not all that big. I had just recently left my position as maternity sister in the busy maternity unit in the nearby town of Minton. One day while he was on his ward round, Dr Munro had persuaded me to join him and his team with his enthusiasm and excitement as to what the new practice could offer. 'Just the thing, now you are getting married,' he had stated. 'Working social hours instead of shift work and no weekend duties,' he had emphasised. Then, knowing I was getting married and would be waiting for the completion of our house to go through, as a second bonus he had added, 'You can have the flat above the surgery until your house is ready.'

This had sealed any doubts in my mind about the practice I had chosen, because, Dr O'Leary, the senior partner from the 'opposition' had approached me at the end of one of his visits to the maternity unit a week after I accepted the offer from Boweryhill Surgery, and he had not concealed his look of disapproval when I declined his offer and told him I was going to work for Dr Munro. I felt a little uncomfortable letting Dr O'Leary down. After all he was my family doctor, and inevitably I would be visiting him as a patient in the future. Both doctors had been looking for an experienced nurse to mould and develop this new role in nursing called 'the practice nurse'.

'Oh! Come through,' said the receptionist. 'My name is Pam.'

Her attitude had changed to a more friendly and subdued one as she opened the door leading behind the reception area.

9

'Old For New'

Boweryhill Surgery was established in 1945 (the year I was born) in a house in Black Wood, by Dr Young, who worked from a converted room in his home. Working alongside him were Bert his dispenser and his partner Dr Munro, who first moved to the area in 1952 after graduation from Glasgow University in 1950. Sadly Dr Young, who was a very popular family doctor loved by the community he served, died suddenly, leaving a grieving population of patients who marked his memory by having a stained glass window inserted in St Stephen's Church, Black Wood opposite his home. Dr Munro was treasurer of the church and was also a driving force behind the building of the church hall.

The loss of the senior partner left Dr Munro, his young partner, to run the practice. He was later joined by Dr Samuels, then in 1961 they were fortunate to have Dr Blessington start as a trainee in the practice, who with his wife moved to live in Black Wood. Over the next few years the practice took on more doctors to cope with the growing demand for care, leaving the current premises wanting.

In 1969 when the practice had expanded enough to move to its new purpose-built surgery in the local town of Bendigo, the staff comprised of five GP partners: Dr Munro, Dr Samuels, Dr Blessington, Dr Turnball and Dr Gardener; in addition, a receptionist/secretary, dispenser, part-time nurse and me, a full-time nurse.

This was a time when the government had brought about a new way in which the services of the National Health Service had to be delivered in the community for the benefit of the population, at the same time as offering the general practitioners a choice on how they could work together in a group to help improve patient care. They as doctors would gain by being able to share in the workload as opposed to working alone in their individual practices, as had been the case in years gone by.

One choice the doctors had was to combine with other GPs in the area in a health centre where the premises would be owned by the local authorities which would have the majority of the control as to how the health centres would be run and who the clerical and nursing staff would be that worked there. The local authority would be the body that financed the centre, therefore they stood to gain the higher percentage of any financial profits which could be expected to occur.

The other choice the GPs had was to buy their own premises and form their own practices with the local authority financing 75 per cent of the staff salaries, and although the Family Health Service Association (FHSA) as it was then known still had a say in how the practice population should be served in certain aspects of health issues, it was on the whole up to the individual surgeries to say how they wanted to run their practice. And depending on the doctors themselves and how they worked, they could prove to be financially profitable or not.

The doctor's of Boweryhill Surgery decided to keep their independence and chose to buy their own premises. This also gave them the freedom as to who they wanted to employ and in doing so they had better control of the running of the practice, introducing their own style of service to their patients and the way in which it was delivered, with control of its financial benefits.

The patients endured many changes when the practice moved to Bendigo, both in the way the practice was run and the new services that were being introduced. Not surprisingly, the first two weeks proved to be chaos. The patients had in the past been use to just turning up at Black Wood practice where they were prepared to wait until the doctor saw them, however long that might be but they were assured that they would always be seen. So introducing the patients to a new appointment system met with disapproval from the locals to say the least. Trying to bring about change, where they had to make an appointment to be seen or be turned away at the reception desk if there was not a free appointment available, after the Black Wood practice had run on a 'come and wait to be seen' idea, was in the early weeks at Hill Street a nightmare for both the patients and the medical and clerical staff alike.

The introduction of the practice nurse was a new aspect of general practice, as in the past the doctors themselves had carried out all treatments for their patients from applying a bandage to giving them injections. Now, in an attempt to lessen the workload for the doctors, the practice nurse was employed to carry out all nursing tasks and in doing so create more time for the doctors to see patients that needed to be seen by them. By moving into this new discipline of nursing I was privileged to become one of the first practice nurses established in Shropshire, and gradually over the weeks, months and years was one of the instigators of developing the role of the practice nurse.

This included the setting up of various clinics within the practice which enabled the patients to make appointments to see the nurse to have such things as their blood pressure checked or cervical smears taken, diabetic checks, or their asthma monitored, to mention just a few. At the same time this opened up an opportunity for the practice nurse to give advice on lifestyle changes or counselling if necessary, to which the patients responded well. They were keen to gain knowledge and be educated on any aspect of change that might enhance their health long term.

Introducing changes worked both ways: it gave the medical staff – practice nurses and GPs – an opportunity to develop their own professional development, and it was essential that they attended study days to gain knowledge of the latest research and treatments in medicine to benefit the people they served. The patients gained the benefits of this new-found knowledge and at the same time it gave them the opportunity to question any new findings as well as the advantage of expressing to the medical staff their needs as they saw them to be, and then hopefully seeing them met.

One such example was that ladies within the practice who had had a hysterectomy felt the need for some sort of counselling either prior or after such an operation to help them cope with the mental effects of losing their Womanhood.

Having grasped this new challenge and enjoying the work involved, the delight had to be the characters I met and grew to love who came through the doors of what was then the state-of-the-art surgery. This had two floors; the ground level consisted of a waiting room which had an impressive contemporary wall cleverly covered with cut-outs from magazines, newspapers and pictures. This proved, in the years that followed, to keep many a patient interested while they waited for the doctor to call them. One door from the waiting room entered into the large treatment room; this also was the only access the staff had to the reception area. The only other door leading off from the waiting room led on to the long corridor with doors on each side of it. At the beginning on the left was Bert's dispensary; the others were toilets, store cupboards, six consultant rooms each with adjoining doors, and the door at the end of the corridor led to the stairs access for the floor above.

On the upper level were two flats; occupying one was both a friend and patient of one of the partners, a lady corset fitter, who in the years that followed squeezed many an odd shape into sizes smaller than nature intended. The other flat, which had been offered to me by Dr Munro when he had first persuaded me to join the practice, remained vacant until a new trainee doctor was employed. I on the other hand moved into our new house, ten minutes' walk away, earlier than expected so had no need to take up his offer.

Little did we know then what our new house had in store for us as a newly married couple, and leaving work one Friday no one could have guessed what a difference a weekend would bring.

It was 4th January 1971; we had been married just 16 months when it all happened. Our alarm clock was set to go off for 7 a.m. and just five minutes beforehand, we were awoken by a terrific explosion that lifted off part of the roof, followed by another explosion that shook the house causing rubble and debris to fall around us. My first thoughts on waking out of a deep sleep were that a plane had crashed through the roof. What other explanation could there be? I was lying in bed, completely stunned, looking at the sky. However we were fortunate to have still been in bed, as we discovered later that the only patch of ceiling still in place in the lounge below was the piece supporting the bed we were in.

The events that followed seemed like a nightmare and the place looked like something from the Blitz. There were broken windows, internal doors off their hinges, and part of the floor missing. Instantly Keith jumped out of bed and I followed, only to feel the pain of broken glass and debris under my bare feet. Being a good husband, Keith quickly took control and somehow found me a pair of slippers and a coat in spite of all the chaos, before helping me down what was left of the stairs.

By this time there were people everywhere. Many were our neighbours, and one of the first on the scene was Dr Turnball, ordering me to get out before the next gas explosion. At this stage no one knew whether or not every house in Fairview Road was about to blow up, and understandably everyone was in a state of panic, soon relieved by the quick response from the emergency services who within minutes of it happening were on the scene.

Sunday, the day before the disaster, had been a very cold day with freezing fog, the type of day when no one ventures out unless absolutely necessary. So when an 8-inch gas main in our garden fractured and gas was leaking into the street, no one smelt the gas, so we were not aware of it until the following morning when a man was on his way to work. He was walking past our house smoking a cigarette at the time when he smelt and felt the pressure of gas around his ankles. The man, although in a state of fear, used his initiative and ran down to the police station in Bendigo to report it.

Straight away a policeman came up to Fairview Road to investigate. The PC had just reached the cul-de-sac and was in the road outside our house at the same time as Bob, the man next door who had got up for work, was in the process of making a cup of tea. But as Bob pulled the plug out of the electric socket the spark caused by the action ignited the gas which surrounded the property, with the whole of the cavity walls being full of gas. The neighbour's house was destroyed, causing irrevocable damage to the two adjoining houses, one of which was ours. The policeman fortunately was unhurt even although the badge on the front of his helmet was blown off with the force of the blast; he was later awarded the Queen's Medal for Bravery.

But for the grace of God, no one was killed or badly hurt apart from Bob our neighbour who was taken to hospital with hand burns, but we were all grateful that although three houses had been destroyed and had to be rebuilt, which was bad enough, no lives, which are more important, had been lost. Amazingly, even the neighbour's elderly mother who lived with them, and had her head sticking through their rafters as a result of the blast and who had been shouting for help, managed to escaped unharmed. The blast was so powerful that it broke windows in Bendigo town centre and could be heard as far as Daisywood, 4 miles away, causing the public at large to speculate what it might be until the media informed them, when the news then became the talk of the place.

The neighbours and I were taken to Dr Turnball's home further along Fairview Road while Keith stayed with the rescue team where he was able to help carry out the next-door neighbours from the debris that once, up until a few minutes earlier, had been their home. I remember Dr Munro coming from Black Wood and arriving in Dr Turnball's lounge, where I sat wearing nothing more than a nightdress under a duffel coat, and after taking a look around him at the emotional condition we were all in, he generously told me, 'Take the day off today.'

The fact that my home and possessions had been blown to smithereens had not occurred to him – the show must go on.

Although the external walls of our house still stood, most of the roof had been ripped off and the interior of the house was demolished. However Keith's watch, which when he took it off was always left upstairs on our dressing table at night, was found later inside what was left of the fridge in the kitchen downstairs at the other end of the house. Some months later I wrote to Timex the watch maker to tell the company how the watch had survived the blast and still kept good time.

Timex later sent a photographer who captured Keith wearing the watch at work while he was giving driving lessons to his pupils. This photo was used at a later date in the *Timex Magazine* as an advert promoting the reliability of their watches; at the same time it did no harm in advertising Keith's driving school.

The reality of the blast meant we had to move in with my in-laws in Jackend until our house could be rebuilt. Fortunately for us they had plenty of room to accommodate us and were happy to do so. I had been off work one week when Dr Munro called to see me and during his visit he advised that the best thing for me would be to get back to work to take my mind off things at home. I took his advice and returned to work after a week that had turned our lives upside down, and I had to admit that Dr Munro was right: treating patients and helping them deal with their problems helped me to cope with mine and it was the best way to get back to normal.

In August of that year we moved back into our newly built house which was fitted once again with gas central heating, having been assured by the builder that because of the excessive inspections of the property carried out by the various authorities during the rebuilding, it should be one of the safest houses in the road. Hopefully lightning does not strike twice in the same place!

Some months after I had started at the practice Sue joined the team, employed as the medical secretary. I had first seen Sue when she worked as a medical secretary at the Tinto Hospital, taking dictation for the consultants at the end of their outpatients' clinic. I had seen her as she passed the maternity unit on her way to the outpatients' department around the corner: she was distinctive with her fashionable long, pointed umbrella which she used as a walking stick when it wasn't raining.

During the time we worked at the surgery together we became good friends both at work and socially after work. Sue and John had been married six months after Keith and I and our husbands were both members of the Bendigo Round Table; as their wives we were entitled to become members of the Bendigo Ladies Circle (a branch of a nationwide charity organisation) if we wanted to, which we did.

The Round Table members were comprised of a variety of young businessmen who at reaching the age of 40 had to leave Table, keeping the charity a young man's club. The function of both charities, Table and Circle, was to raise monies to be used for the benefit of the local community and those in need.

In the process of raising funds for the charity we as members organised a lot of social events throughout the year which we thoroughly enjoyed taking part in, either in the form of a dinner dance followed by a cabaret or fun-raising sports events involving the public. Here we would have stalls selling items of something or other and a variety of things including raffle tickets for prizes to be won.

One weekend Keith and I travelled to Cannock to a charity fair where we had booked a stand selling raffle tickets for the prize of a football. Keith and I had set up our stand in front of our car where we had put dozens of balls in a net fixed to the doors of the car to hold it in place. The sight of the mountain of footballs brought the crowd flocking like bees to a honey pot. We could not sell the tickets quick enough, and in no time we had given away all the footballs, but the public had us pinned against our car clamouring for more tickets. Wondering why the people still wanted to buy tickets, we insisted at the top of our voices that all the prizes had gone.

When eventually we managed to get through to some of the people they pushed back and asked, 'What about the car?'

Because the balls had gone, they presumed the large cardboard sign which said 'Buy a Ticket and Win', referrred to the car. With the force of the crowd it had fallen from its original position and its big red arrow pointing downwards was now leaning on the roof of our car. Amazingly we got out of there in one piece, carrying a record amount of funds collected to go towards the new Colbolt Unit in Shrewsbury for the treatment of cancer.

Sue and I shared many a dance routine practising with some of the other ladies in the Circle as we prepared for yet another cabaret. Fortunately, because one of our members had been a professional dancer as one of the Tiller Girls on television in the past, she was now our choreographer at these dance practices. She often expected great things from us, things that to her exasperation were rarely delivered.

However Bendigo Ladies Circle were once selected to put on a dance routine in the cabaret at the Midsummer Ball (the biggest Circle event of the year) held in Wolverhampton. That night we danced to the music of 'Hey Big Spender' and after a quick change on stage we transformed our costumes to perform to the music of 'We're in the Army Now', The evening turned out to be a great success, much to the delight of our Tiller Girl.

Our friendship continued, but our working relationship came to an end when Sue became pregnant and left the surgery to have her baby girl, Vanessa. The night she was born John, her dad, celebrated the birth of his daughter by having a few friends join him for a meal at a local restaurant. In the party, apart from Keith and myself, there was Sheila, the other practice nurse at the time, and her husband Henry, and Brenda with her husband, another Keith.

Brenda had worked alongside Sue at the surgery as a second secretary before Sue left, and as we all got on well at work it was quite normal for the eight of us to go out together on occasions. The night the baby was born everyone came back to our house for coffee after the meal out. John was slightly the worse for wear after wetting the baby's head a little too often during the evening so my Keith, after bidding our friends goodnight, drove John back to his home in his car and I followed in ours to bring Keith home.

When Keith arrived at John's home and got out of the car to open the garage doors, John got out of the passenger side and stood in the middle of the main road to direct the traffic. To my surprise as I turned the corner into the Daisywood Road I was faced with trying to avoid running over this very happy new daddy.

Eventually we got him safely indoors where we headed him towards his bedroom door, then left knowing he was safe at home while his wife nursed their new baby in hospital, unaware of it all. Or so we thought until early the next morning when our telephone, rang with Sue at the other end asking, 'Keith, have you any idea where John's car is?'

John had woken and looked out of the window and could not see his car on the drive, and as he could not remember what had happened the night before, never mind where he had left his car, in a panic he had rang Sue in hospital to tell her he had lost the car. She, on the other hand, had been more upset that she had missed out on a good night out, and rang in annoyance.

'Yes, Sue, it's in your garage,' Keith reassured her before going back to sleep.

Meanwhile Brenda, who had been wearing new shoes on our night out had apparently been sick on them on her way home and the following morning in a desperate attempt to clean her latest buy had flushed her shoes down the toilet. Although she did manage to retrieve them she had caused a lot of commotion in doing so. Thankfully such celebrations were few and far between. A little later I was thrilled if not a little surprised to be asked by Sue and John if I would be Vanessa's godmother; the surprise element came from thinking that if anyone would have been approached to have the pleasure of such an honour, it might have been Keith, who every time he saw Vanessa had never failed to be fascinated by such a lovely baby.

I was not fully aware what duties a godmother had, and only hoped I would be able to fulfil them whatever they might be, but I have to confess I did not do much as the family eventually moved from Shropshire to live in Dorset.

10

Fellow Scot

The senior partner, Dr Munro (a fellow Scot of medium build and height), although a kind and caring man was known for always being in a rush, so much so that it was even said by some of his regular patients that he had written out their repeat prescription before they had reached his room with their problems.

I realised just how right they were about him rushing when I went into Dr Munro's room one morning to ask him for a prescription for someone I was dealing with, in the treatment room, and I entered just after a patient had come out from seeing him.

'Oh, what's that smell?' I asked, thinking poor doctor having to deal with that odour first thing in the morning.

'Oh! That's the two boiled eggs I have in my pocket,' he replied, taking them out. 'I hadn't time for breakfast this morning.'

Here was me thinking it was the patient he had seen, who by the way had made a dive for the front door to get some fresh air back into his lungs after inhaling such dreadful fumes coming up from the good doctor's pocket. Goodness only knows what the patient thought the smell was – he never stopped to ask. But whatever his health problems were that morning the visit to Dr Munro had assured the patient that his nose had not been affected.

Dr Munro regarded himself as a quick learner and was eager to put into practice any new methods, tasks or treatments. One Monday morning after the doctor had attended a weekend course on manipulation he buzzed for his first appointment, an unsuspecting patient who slowly and painfully entered Dr Munro room complaining of a stiff neck, causing his head to lean to the right.

'Doctor, I have a terrible stiff neck and can't straighten it,' groaned the patient.

The doctor looked up from his desk and grasping the opportunity said, 'Don't worry, I have just been on a weekend course for manipulation and can carry out my new skills on you; I'll fix you in no time.'

A few minutes later the patient was seen departing a little quicker than he had arrived but still in discomfort with his head leaning to the left; his parting words as he left the GP's room were, 'Thanks, doctor, but I won't be back until you have finished the course.'

Dr Munro was delighted that he had tried out his latest new skill and was quite pleased he had been able to help, and that the man would be back for some follow up treatment.

I understood there had been some humour in the past, and some of Dr Munro's elderly patients told me of the time Dr Munro did a home visit on horseback, and his horse ate the patient's well-groomed hedge while the doctor was inside the house attending the now agitated patient, who could see what was happening from his bedroom window and could not do anything about it due to his condition.

The horse, on the other hand had not only enjoyed its exercise for the day, but had gained an extra titbit as well. The mishap never deterred the patient, who always requested that (his favourite doctor) Dr Munro, came on any future home visits. Although I do believe the horse had made its one and only visit to that particular hedge.

The only female partner in those days was Dr Turnball, a tall, sophiscated young lady who knew her patients and their families well, never forgetting their names. She was always in demand by the female population of the practice due to her understanding, and being of the same gender was able to relate to their needs more than a male GP. Like her partners she was known for implementing an up-to-date knowledge of medicine wherever needed. She was also good to work for, being very approachable and easy to talk to, and because she was young herself we as nurses could relate to her with confidence. Although she did not tolerate fools easily and when she appeared in surgery the staff attended to their work with a new lease of life, sometimes creating jobs just to look busy.

The first encounter I had with Dr Turnball was when she attended my wedding as a guest, afterwards we were neighbours as she lived with her parents in the same road as me just a few houses away. Funnily enough, Keith had fancied buying their house when it came on the market prior to them having it, but he decided it was too expensive for our budget at that time so we settled for the one down the road with three bedrooms instead of four.

Shortly after the practice moved from Black Wood, Dr Munro married Dr Turnball. The wedding was a grand affair at St Paul's Church Staffordshire, where the service was more on the lines of a royal affair with at least five hymns sung between the service address. The wedding reception was held at a beautiful hotel where the food and drink were in great supply: needless to say the surgery staff (most of whom attended) enjoyed the party. The fashion of the day was the mini skirt, where it was a case of bending one's knee rather than bending one's back when picking up anything that had been dropped on the floor. After a few drinks most of the ladies forgot the rule of the knee bending and some of the sights that followed were as the saying goes, 'a sight for sore eyes'.

After their wedding Dr Munro and Dr Turnball left Boweryhill Surgery and moved up to Scotland where Dr Munro set up the first medical practice in the New Town of Stovey and where his wife Dr Turnball joined him as a partner in the practice at a later date once the new surgery had expanded.

The head of Boweryhill Surgery then became Dr Samuels, and with two doctors now gone there was a need to find replacements. This is when Dr Daffin not only joined the team but also, conveniently for all concerned, he bought Dr Munro's house which had been the original practice in Black Wood. A few weeks later the second vacant position was taken by Dr

Cummingham, so once again our complement of doctors was complete, and although there had been changes in the practice with a few of the doctors, some of the original staff remained loyal.

Bert was the dispenser, who had worked for the practice since the beginning of time, and what Bert did not know about the patients was not worth knowing; he in turn was known and liked by them. Bert was a local man, and away from work he mixed with the community socially as a committee member of the local football team where he organised most social events, many of which I was asked to attend as a guest of Dr Samuels' (after his first wife died) who was there to present the trophies to the players.

At work Bert was notorious for his knowledge of pills and potions and many a time he would question the doctor's prescription given for a particular individual, who Bert knew (or at least thought he did) would benefit more from some other medication that the patient had been given in the past. Bert was famous for his Woodbine cigarettes which he was very rarely seen without (there was no law about smoking then) and, just as rarely, was he able to complete a sentence without swearing. Then in between times he would sing hymns as he moved about the dispensary.

Once I got used to his various ways, Bert and I got on well. In fact, it was his constant persistence that encouraged me to go back to work at the surgery after my maternity leave, when all I really wanted to do was stay and be a full-time mum to the baby we had decided to have after five years of marriage.

One day Bert (who was small in stature) was walking along the corridor in front of Dr Samuels who was taller and had a heavier physique – which Bert was about to discover. Dr Samuels caught his hand on the door hinge as he came into the surgery, causing him to sustain a small cut that started to bleed. The sight of his own blood caused Dr Samuels to faint and fall on Bert's back. This resulted in a flow of choice words from Bert who was unaware that the doctor had just fainted and thought Dr Samuels was playing the fool. The full weight of Dr Samuels flattened Bert to the floor, thus cushioning the doctor's fall. Eventually Bert managed to squeeze his way out from under Dr Samuels' body and get to his feet, still puffing and blowing but eager to check that the doctor was OK. Believe me, it was a long time before Bert allowed Dr Samuels to forget that the minor injury he had sustained had made him – a doctor – react so dramatically by fainting.

The truth was that Bert thought the world of Dr Samuels, and at every given opportunity he would invite the doctor to be the guest of honour at the many local football cup presentation nights. Here Dr Samuels would make the presentations after delivering an appropriate after-dinner speech to the guests and footballers, many of who were also his patients and held him in high regard. It was on some of these special evenings that Keith and I had the privilege of accompanying Dr Samuels and witnessing first hand the respect and admiration the community had for their GP, as he handed over their trophies to them.

Over the years that Bert and I worked together we became good friends, and his knowledge of the community we served proved to be helpful to me when I came in contact with them, since knowing their background was at times useful in the treatment of them. Bert enjoyed his work, and although he did not really trust anyone else to do his job while he was on holiday, he did (on the rare occasion he took his holiday) allow me to fill the gap until he returned. I always felt this was a privilege, because with the unrest that occurred in the early days of moving into Bendigo Bert had become more protective of his job, and rightly so.

The reason for this was that back in the days of Black Wood Surgery it was allowed by what was then known as the Family Health Service Association (FHSA) that if a practice was situated a mile or more from the nearest town it could have its own dispensary, in order to enable registered patients who also lived a mile from the nearest chemist to collect their prescriptions without having to travel too far to get them. However when the practice moved to the premises in Bendigo this situation no longer needed to apply, but because Bert was an established member of the surgery staff, the FHSA agreed that as long as Bert was employed the dispensary would be allowed to remain.

This caused quite a threat and certainly unsettlement and a little hostility from a few of the chemists in Bendigo, because they feared our dispensing would have an effect on their financial income, knowing that dispensing prescriptions brought in a good profit to their business. It was obvious that it was easier for a patient to come out of a doctor's consulting room, walk down the corridor and collect his or her medication before leaving the surgery, rather than trail into town to the various chemists where they would sometimes have to queue and wait for their prescription to be dispensed before walking back down the road either to their parked car, or to catch the bus – where the bus stop was just outside the surgery.

Over the years I became very close to Bert and his wife Kath, more so when he took ill, and in the weeks before he died, I would spend a lot of time with them, keeping him in touch with the goings-on at the surgery during his absence.

The sad thing about having a little knowledge was that Bert during his illness was only too aware of the medication he was prescribed and the side-effects that accompanied it; he knew what the next stage of his illness would bring and this made it difficult for those who cared for him.

Both he and Kath received amazing support from friends and family alike during this period. Their house, which was situated in the heart of the community which he had served, was rarely empty of well-wishers offering practical help.

Now practical help was needed when it came to making a difference to the state of the surgery, so after having looked at the tartan wallpaper on one wall in the waiting room for a few years, Mabel (one of the other practice nurses) and I decided to change it. After all it had been Dr Blessington who, in an attempt to make me feel at home after missing my fellow Scot (Dr Munro), had chosen tartan to replace the magazine cuttings originally on the wall. As the tartan that greeted me every working morning became a little worn and tatty the idea of changing it was a good one; also because, being Scottish, I would have preferred to have been looking at my own family tartan – other tartans from someone else's clan don't mean a thing.

Mabel and I agreed that the best time to bring about the change would be on a Saturday afternoon after the emergency surgery finished, which was just before lunchtime. Once we had picked an 'easy on the eye' wallpaper and fixed a date that suited us both we set to, changing the look of the waiting area.

As we scrapped and stripped the old tartan off the wall we did so under the eyes of many of the patients who were passing the surgery on their way to do their weekend shopping, but had now gathered and were peering through the windows. They were waiting the off-chance of getting into the surgery, where they could then perhaps be able to grasp an opportunity to ask advice or get out-of-appointment treatment, which might save them having to take time off work for a visit in the week.

But knowing the patients as we did and how they would take advantage of having the free time on a Saturday to talk to us (oblivious that this was our day off), there was no way that we intended to unlock the surgery door to let them in. If we had, the wall would never have got finished before surgery on Monday morning. I did manage to unlock the doors at one stage to escape into Bendigo to buy some fish and chips for our lunch – this was a much-needed energy boost which enabled us to finish the task, even if the slight aroma of vinegar along with the smell that came from the freshly decorated waiting room did linger for a short time into the start of the next week. However the decor lasted a lot longer.

Not that everyone took any notice of the efforts that had been made to try and add some glamour to the place. The staff admired The Wall which they could not avoid looking at every time they approached the reception desk, but some of our younger patients could not be expected to give the fancy wallpaper a second glance especially when they had more important things on their minds such as trying to bunk off school.

11

All in a Morning's Work

Monday morning and the door of the surgery burst open with force as Bob, a red-faced boy, barged in and breathlessly asked, 'Can I see the doctor?'

Seeing the state he was in the receptionist sent him without hesitation down the corridor to the doctor's room. Bob ran without stopping until he reached the doctor's door, where he then charged in, panicking.

'Doctor, my heart stopped on my way to school and I had to run to start it.'

Now this was the last thing the doctor wanted to deal with at the start of a busy day ahead. Bob was a young boy who he knew well, and who would do anything to dodge school. Being duty bound the doctor took a quick look at the cunning lad, before taking the rascal by the scruff of his neck and marching him back down the corridor, through the waiting room to the front door of the surgery where the now frustrated doctor was heard to say as he ushered young Bob through, 'Now you have given it a kick-start, keep running and don't stop until you reach the school gates.'

Despite the fact that Bob missed school whenever he got the chance, he grew up to become a successful local businessman, which goes to prove that it is not always what you know but how you use and apply your knowledge that can make a difference in life. However as an adult he remained neurotic and some years later was admitted to hospital.

When he was being transferred from the trolley to the bed he asked the nurse, 'Now I am in bed, do I look any better?'

The nurse took one look at him and said, 'What in five minutes?' Then in exasperation, 'Miracles take a little longer.'

But some miracles can happen – if we try hard enough – as was the case in the early years at Boweryhill Surgery (1986) in the days when patients who had been taken unwell unexpectedly could just turn up at the surgery on the same day in the hope of seeing a doctor. Nine times out of ten there was no problem in them getting an appointment. And during these early days before computers were installed there were times when the staff on the odd occasion had a few minutes' free time between appointments. It was on such a day that I felt it was time for us to try and get to know our neighbouring practice, the other medical surgery in Bendigo and perhaps in doing so we could improve the social relationship we had with those we called 'The Opposition'.

The reason for this term was that the new surgeries had opened within weeks of each other, with both groups of doctors from each practice eager to increase their patient list (which was necessary for financial benefit) and working hard to do so. Inevitably there was a little rivalry between the surgeries with the individual practices endeavouring to impress the population in an attempt to encourage them to register at the practice. At the same time the doctors were hoping to be able to choose the patients they wanted on their list. However, apart from this not being realistic it was not possible, because each surgery was given a specific catchment area by the Shropshire Health Authority and the surgery population had to come from within that area.

Good relationships between surgeries are essential, especially when they are neighbours in the same town. This was the reason that, in a moment of impulse, I phoned up The Venal Medical Practice out of the blue and challenged them to a rounders match with our practice. After they had got over thinking I was more than a little crazy to even suggest such a thing, while at the same time trying not to sound rude over the phone, their response came back as a surprised, 'We don't play rounders.'

Determined not to be put off to easily I persuaded then, 'Neither do we, but we can have a go.'

Eventually, after exchanging a few phone calls throughout the next few days the challenge was taken up: the only other thing to do was to agree on the date we would have the match, then to go ahead and plan the evening. It was decided that we would first of all play the rounders match, then complete the evening with a barbeque in my garden. With both sets of staff from each practice now looking forward to the challenge I set to and arranged the venue for the first match, which we agreed would be held on The common in Bendigo where there was plenty of open space to run around in, and the location would be well out of sight from the public we served: this proved to be ideal as it was within walking distance of my home.

Having walked up the common to view the layout of the match ground, the first thing I had to do was to contact the County Council and after explaining what we intended to do, I asked them if they would kindly cut the thigh-high grass on this area prior to the match. After all was said and done, this was a public area where many folks enjoyed taking their dogs for a walk. Unfortunately, despite my plea, the council informed me that I had not given them enough warning so they had not got the time to cut the grass before the date of the match. But they assured me they would try to oblige next time, if there was to be a next time.

As it turned out the long grass proved to add to the fun of the night, causing the running between the stumps to be difficult with the teams having to use more of an effort. Our practice staff delighted in seeing Dr Blessington come into his own when he showed his skills in bowling, and how he could run, before disappearing head-first into the long grass as he dived for the ball. This was a sight to behold. Whereas Dr Samuels did not do any running, but showed off his own skills in his bowling action and the speed of the ball hitting the posts to knock our opponents out of the game as they attempted to outrun the oncoming ball.

The Samuels Ball Trophy was a rounders ball professionally mounted on top of a plinth, the base of which was surrounded with blank brass name discs ready for engraving at a future date. The trophy, which was aptly named after Dr Samuels, the head of the practice, was ours that night.

After the match 40 now weary staff from both surgeries (including their partners) attended the barbeque that followed. With the help of some of my friends I had managed to borrow enough garden tables and chairs to accommodate everyone; when we arrived back at the garden we were met by the aroma of tasty meats, thanks to some of my friends who had started the barbeque and were already cooking the food.

The laughter and chat that followed continued into the night, marking the first match as a great success; from then on the rounders match between The Boweryhill Surgery and The Venal Medical Practice became an event which continued for a number of years. The venue varied each year, depending on the winning team from the previous year, who then acted as host by making the arrangements and providing the food at the end of the match.

One year our practice (which was responsible for the medical care of the soldiers and their families) had this mad idea of challenging the Army staff at the garrison to a rounders match: which we did. Needless to say the Army are not known for turning down a challenge, especially from a team of unfit civilians, the majority of whom were women. So it was a great shock to them when, to our delight and disbelief, we came out victorious. I have to say it was more chance than skill that won the match for us that night.

However the ego boost we had from the win only made the Army team more determined to set up a return challenge of their choice in the near future. There was no way that we were going to refuse to take up their challenge, which was at a laser shooting gallery in Minton. Once we were inside the gallery the two teams had to creep around in the dark armed with their laser gun weapons to find the enemy and shoot them with the laser rays. The guns automatically registered how many shots had been fired and also how many hits the individuals had received. By the end of the fun evening most of our staff were registered as being riddled with holes, while the Army staff who had used their training to the full by keeping their backs against the wall had came out as one would expect – victorious.

There was always some sort of happenings going on at the Army camp; sometimes it was more dramatic than sport. The one incident that comes to mind was one Tuesday morning in March when I was dealing with an antenatal clinic in the treatment room located just inside the main entrance to the Medical Reception Station, when I heard the main swing doors to the Station thrown open and someone shouting, 'Medical Emergency!'

The next thing that I knew was that the door to the treatment room burst open and I saw a man (whom I later found out to be a Mr Dunn) being assisted into the room by a policeman. In fact the policeman was actually holding Mr Dunn up. Mr Dunn at this time was in a state of collapse, being ashen in colour, finding it difficult to breathe, and was unable to communicate. At this point I believed that he was in the process of having a heart attack, and that in my medical experience he was a true emergency.

I sat Mr Dunn onto a chair and spoke to him, trying to establish his medical history, and if he was on any medication, or suffered from asthma or chest pains. I attempted to get Mr Dunn onto the examination couch but due to his breathless state this proved impossible. However I then went on to administer oxygen, and asked one of the Army nurses to ring for an ambulance and to contact the duty doctor on call for the Boweryhill Surgery that day.

While the nurse was on the telephone I then went on to try and take Mr Dunn's blood pressure. It was then, as I tried to roll up the sleeve of his blue jumper, that I discovered his clothes were wet. Because of this and the abrasions Mr Dunn had to his face I actually thought that the man may have been drowning. As I was reassuring him he told me that his face had not been under water at all.

The Army nurse appeared in the room and assisted me in getting Mr Dunn onto the examination couch. Having the nurse present gave me the opportunity to leave the treatment room to speak to the duty doctor on the telephone, and I informed him that Mr Dunn had numerous medical conditions. I went on to say that I had sent for an ambulance and had administered oxygen. The doctor reassured me that I was taking the right course of action.

I went on to tell the doctor that Mr Dunn was not one of our patients but that he was in fact registered at another practice in another area of Shropshire.

I returned to the treatment room and spoke to Mr Dunn, who by now looked a little better, and asked, 'Where is my wife?'

The paramedics from the local health authority arrived at the treatment room, and it was at this point that the patient complained of blurred vision and said that he could not see properly. He then put his head against the paramedic who stood to the right of the couch and said, 'I'm going.'

With this his eyes glazed over and he appeared to semi-faint. Once again he asked for his wife, and resigned himself to going into hospital. Just then a woman entered the treatment room who turned out to be Mrs Dunn.

Taking the opportunity I explained to Mrs Dunn that her husband needed to go into hospital. 'He doesn't like hospitals,' she replied

Well, who does, I thought as I left the room to speak to the on call doctor again, and give him an update that the paramedics had arrived and that the patient was going to go into hospital. On my return to the treatment room Mr Dunn was being lifted onto the trolley by the paramedics and his wife was no longer in the room.

As the ambulance pulled away from the Army camp I walked towards the car park and as I entered my car to make my way back to the surgery in Bendigo I was puzzled as to what had happened that day to Mr Dunn, because as far as I was aware there were no pools, or rivers near by for him to accidentally fall into.

As I drove away from the camp, I remembered when I myself nearly drowned. It happened some years earlier, before I was married, when I was working as a midwife. Mike, one of the neighbours at that time, offered to teach me to swim. As I had always wanted to learn, I grasped the opportunity and went with him to the swimming baths one evening after work.

'There is nothing to it,' said Mike. 'The easiest and quickest way to learn is to dive in at the deepest end and you will automatically float to the surface and swim.'

Doubting his instructions, I hesitated as I stood at the edge of the deep end of the baths.

'Don't worry about jumping in, I'll catch you,' he called from the water below me.

Knowing he was a good swimmer, I jumped into the water before I had a chance to think about what I was doing. I hit the cold water and sank to the bottom of the pool and, as my feet touched the bottom, I bounced back to the surface. Panic stricken, and gasping for breath because the water had gone straight up my nose, I lashed out at something to grab hold of, which turned out to be Mike's bare back.

As Mike struggled to reach the edge of the baths, with me clinging like mad to his back, he was not so sure he was as good a swimmer as he first thought. When we reached the side and got out of the water, Mike's back looked as if a cat had attacked him; it had several long scratches from his shoulders to his waist where I had drawn blood, caused by me digging my fingernails into his flesh in my attempt to hang on. Strangely enough, he never did offer to take me swimming again.

12

The Gentlemen

Dr Samuels, second in line to the empire, was a loveable homely man with a caring bedside manner that made him a good GP, sensitive to his patients' needs. It was not unlike him to sit up all night at the bedside of a sick patient, then arrive to start his surgery the next day without a mention to anyone that he had had no sleep. Because he was so human in his approach to all he came in contact with, both patients and staff found Dr Samuels easy to talk to, and this they did not only about health but anything. He would regularly call to visit one of his patients at their home without warning, just to check if they were OK: his display of genuine concern for them made him a real favourite with the community at large.

One day a very pregnant lady came into the practice at the end of the morning surgery. When she arrived at the desk Dr Samuels just happened to be in the reception area, finishing his cup of coffee.

'Doctor, my husband Alan has been gardening and has been stung by a bee,' she panted. 'His face has gone all swollen,' she continued. 'I have come into Bendigo to get my shopping and thought I would call for some advice.'

Dr Samuels, putting down his coffee, reassuringly replied, 'I will call and see him, go and do your shopping.'

Knowing his patients as well as he did there was no need for him to ask her surname or where she lived he knew the address in Jackend.

Once she had left the surgery Dr Samuels called me to bring the 'emergency tray' from the treatment room and, after checking the tray was fully equipped with all that was required, we quickly left the surgery to set off in his car up the hill to Jackend. However, it was lunchtime and there were several cars in front of us, causing a delay in what normally would be a journey taking only a few minutes to reach our destination.

'We will have to hurry,' I said anxiously. 'Will the patient be having an anaphylactic reaction to the sting, Dr Samuels?' I asked.

'It could be the case, but I'll sort him, he will be OK,' Dr Samuels calmly replied.

At last we arrived at Alan's home and without waiting to be asked Dr Samuels knocked on the front door and walked straight in. As we entered the house we found Alan sitting in the lounge on the settee watching the television. He was wearing his vest and shorts and gasping a lot, with a very swollen face and neck he looked all blown up like a barrage balloon. When the doctor asked how he felt the patient complained of difficulty in breathing: this was due to his swollen tongue and throat caused by the bee sting he had sustained.

After a quick examination Dr Samuels, with an air of control, took a needle and syringe from the tray and administered an injection, dispersing the drug very slowly. This he did at the same time as taking Alan's mind off things by chatting to him about his garden. The conversation helped in both relaxing Alan and relieving any concerns that he may have. The obvious physical improvement of the patient was happening before our eyes, as the drug was visibly reducing the swelling of Alan's face and neck, which within minutes soon returned to their normal size.

Satisfied that Alan's condition had improved and that he was back to his normal self again, we said our farewell. Just as we were leaving his wife arrived home heavily laden with shopping which she soon dropped to hug Dr Samuels in gratitude for all he had done.

Dr Samuels took most things in his stride, and he was no stranger to prominent people in high places; he once told me that while he was growing up on occasions Sir Harold Macmillan often gave him a lift to school. Because Dr Samuels was so modest, he never did say whether or not the prominent figure was a family friend or neighbour: nevertheless during Dr Samuels time at Boweryhill Surgery he had not one but two invitations to the Queen's Garden Party.

On one occasion he asked my husband Keith as a friend if he would act as his chauffeur by driving him and his guests – who were his daughter and wife Joyce – to Buckingham Palace. Although Keith was able to drive right up The Mall to the entrance of the palace he was not allowed to enter the grounds of the garden party, but he did find the events and the protocol of such an occasion very interesting. In fact the whole day proved to be a pleasant experience for all of them, and provided a colourful topic of conversation on the journey home.

Joyce was Dr Samuels' second wife. His first was Gloria, whom I met in the early weeks after starting at the surgery when she arrived one morning and organised all the staff and doctors as a group to gather outside the new premises to have our photo taken as a memento. Sadly she had died shortly after the practice had moved to Bendigo, leaving him with his two sons and two daughters, and a donkey they kept in the field adjacent to their garden at the back of the house. The first time I met this donkey was on the day one of Dr Samuels' daughters got married. A number of guests returned to his house after the wedding reception for an extended party, and Dr Samuels took Keith and me down the garden to met the donkey who had come to the fence on seeing his master approach, knowing he would have some treat for him. The treat was Polo mints: apparently the donkey loved them and since the doctor usually had a packet in his pocket it was obviously him who had introduced them to the creature. As soon as the donkey was in reach Dr Samuels held out his handful of mints which were quickly gobbled up: however Dr Samuels was distracted for a second and turned to chat to us just as the donkey reached over to him and bit his neck, ripping his new, expensive white wedding shirt as he did so.

Fortunately, the injury was only a minor abrasion and he was more upset about the damage to his shirt, which I promised to try and repair later.

'That must have been the biggest love bite you have ever had,' I told him.

'Well, it was certainly the most painful,' he remarked.

Because Dr Samuels was involved in many community events outside of work, it opened up some ideal opportunities to encourage him to ask Joyce, who had also lost her husband some years previously, to accompany him as his guest. So it was no surprise that I along with others was an instigator in the match-making between Dr Samuels and Joyce, who obviously enjoyed each other's company. Eventually they announced they were going to marry.

With Dr Samuels also being the medical officer for the Army it was not surprising that he and Joyce had their wedding reception at the Officers' Mess at the garrison, a place where he had often spent some time in relaxing after a heavy day in the practice, and was familiar with and well known by the catering staff. So it was not unexpected that the reception put on by the Army was spectacular: from the food, which was so fancy it could have been mistaken for a ship's cruise, complete with ice sculptures in the centre of the table, to the sherry and wine, which were in endless supply to those who could drink it. Bert and I had a merry time after a sherry or two before our meal, when my beautiful borrowed hat from Aunt May sat a little on the side of my head rather than on the top. After the second sherry, then later into the afternoon, the same hat did its rounds as many of the ladies in the party had a go at modelling it.

A few years later when Dr Samuels announced that he was retiring, the practice members secretly got their heads together to arrange a surprise party for him at the Dury Hotel in Bendigo, where we were able to gather together a group of his friends and colleagues, and as he was a member of the Masonic Lodge, a number of the masons attended. On the night of his party we arranged for a friend to telephone asking him to meet up for a drink. Initially Dr Samuels declined because he did not feel too good – he thought he might be coming down with the flu – but after some persuasion his friend, who went to fetch him, managed to get him to attend. Once Dr Samuels was at the party and saw all his friends his flu symptoms disappeared, leaving him to enjoy his evening.

Once again the surgery had a new head of the practice: with Dr Samuels retired, Dr Blessington was automatically next in line to take his place, and as with most changes in leadership Dr Blessington brought about his own changes. In his own gentle, quiet way he saw the need to improve the look and the facilities of the inside of the building, by having some walls brought down to help enlarge the waiting room area, and to lift the face of it by having it redecorated. He was always looking for ways in which he could improve the service we provided for the patients, and took on board any suggestions the medical or clerical staff had to offer. He encouraged the staff to pull together as a team, the staff in return were only too happy to work for his approval.

Dr Blessington appreciated the work his partners and staff did and never failed to give praise when it was necessary: this played a good part in the working relationship within the practice.

Prior to joining the practice Dr Blessington went to Paris where he worked in the American Hospital. He intended to go for six months and stayed for one year. Working in this hospital with all the famous patients it was probably inevitable that he should meet Paulette (his future wife) over the bed of Maureen O'Hara, the famous red-headed Irish Hollywood star. Dr Blessington has always been known for his good taste and he certainly had taste when he chose Paulette, a dark-haired, petite, pretty French lady.

Dr Blessington, now first in command, was known by patients to be 'The Gentleman'. He certainly had the air and appearance of a gentleman: he was tall, slender, always smartly dressed and together with his quiet gentle manner had a presence that warranted respect.

I knew Dr Blessington from my time as a midwife on the GP

unit in the Tinto Hospital, Minton. In fact the first time we met I was trying on a long false hairpiece (the fashion at that time) when the doctor arrived on the ward to check on the progress of one of his antenatal ladies who was in early labour. Having been taken unawares I did not have time to remove the wig and as we walked along the hospital corridor to the labour ward I could feel my hairpiece slipping down the back of my head. Too embarrassed to remove it in front of him I tried to retain it by adjusting the position of my head, at the same time as trying to concentrate on the doctor's questions. He being the gentleman that he was, pretended not to notice what was happening to my head and that my hair was getting longer as we spoke. However he did a double take when he returned after his afternoon surgery to check on his patient, and saw me with short hair. He had been unaware that a few hours earlier the hair on my head had not been real.

One Monday morning in surgery a young antenatal girl arrived at the reception desk with her dad, who asked if she could see a doctor. The young girl was wearing her coat over her nightdress: this could be seen by the receptionist who took one look at her and sent her straight into see Dr Blessington. A few minutes later the doctor called me to his room. As I entered I could see the young girl was sitting on the edge of her chair and appeared to be quite uncomfortable.

'Take this lady to a room and I will come and examine her in a moment,' said Dr Blessington.

As we left his room he buzzed for his next patient rather than waste time while he waited for me to get the young girl ready.

After having taken one look at this girl I could see she was in labour and headed for the nearest free consulting room (which happened to be opposite Dr Blessington's). I helped her onto the couch, where I was able to examine her to confirm that she was having contractions and in the late stage of labour. The doctor joined us after he had contacted the ambulance and midwives, requesting their assistance along with a delivery bag, a piece of equipment that most surgeries don't have as a routine. While we waited for their arrival we comforted and tried to reassure this young girl who was about to deliver her first baby. We were thrilled with the delivery of our first Boweryhill Surgery Baby, as we christened him, which happened just as the midwives arrived at the surgery in time to take mother and baby off in the ambulance, leaving Dr Blessington and myself to carry on with our routine Monday morning duties.

The other doctors in surgery that morning, especially Dr Daffin who was next door to the 'delivery room', were amazed to hear of the delivery, along with the patients in the full waiting room who had not been disturbed by any unusual events taking place, mainly because the young mother had made very little fuss and certainly very little noise when she was delivering her baby boy. This was a credit to her, considering earlier that morning her dad had taken her to the Tinto Maternity Hospital thinking she was in labour, only to be sent back home again and told to wait because she was not ready to have her baby yet. He was on his way back home from the hospital when he had decided to divert his journey and drive to the surgery because his daughter was still in pain, which she had been in for most of the night and was now showing signs of distress. This explained why she had turned up in her nightgown.

A few weeks later while doing his afternoon surgery Dr Blessington had a phone call from the dentist whose practice was across the road from the surgery. The dentist asked the doctor if he would come over to their practice to checkout a dental patient they had in the chair. The busy doctor, who had a full list of patients waiting to see him, asked me to run across and assess the problem and let him know. When I arrived at the dental practice the receptionist directed me upstairs and as I got to the top of the stairs a door opened and two masked dentists peeped out, one head above the other. 'She's next door,' they said.

They pointed to the door facing me, and puzzled and surprised at their actions I entered the room where I found a very pregnant lady sitting on the dental chair. By now she was in a well-advanced state of labour. The pregnant lady had gone to the dentist to have a filling done and the dentist had administered the local injection to help her relax. The drug administered had caused everything else to relax, including the muscles at the neck of her womb, thus setting her off into an early labour. I hurriedly informed Dr Blessington by phone of the findings and that I did not think it would be too long before the baby would be born; the fact that the mother-to-be was sitting rather than lying was helping to delay the inevitable from happening.

Without hesitation Dr Blessington contacted the ambulance which was quickly on the scene, and as there was no midwife with them when it arrived I travelled with the lady to the maternity unit in Minton, where she was received into the capable hands of the midwives who later informed Dr Blessington that they had delivered the surprised dental patient of a baby girl shortly after her arrival at the hospital.

Dr Blessington was known by his antenatal ladies as 'the doctor with cold hands' – he was aware of this because they told him often enough during the Antenatal Clinic, so in an attempt to make things more comfortable for them he would palpate their tummy through their woolly jumpers so that his cold hands did not come in contact with their bare skin. The result of which was that some of the lumps and bumps felt by Dr Blessington turned out to be the bilberry stitches on their Aran sweaters.

Some talked of how he would look at conditions such as rashes, viewing them closely and studying the spots with interest, so that he would be able to give an accurate diagnosis. He was conscious of the risk of cross infection between patients, so he always examined rashes with gloves on. There was no doubt that Dr Blessington's hygiene was impeccable: I remember witnessing how sterile-conscious he was, when one day after surgery I caught him disinfecting the door handle of his room; not a bad thing as after all we had never heard of the MRSA bug then.

There are some tales that have to be told about this shy man who was yet so bold. Off duty, Dr Blessington was a member of the Minton Lions (charity organisation) and had been known to dress up sometimes as a clown or at other times as an elf and stand up in the Rosebank town centre and shake a can for charity, hoping that his patients would not recognise him and take the opportunity to show him their warts or verrucas before asking for his advice on treatment.

The characters that Dr Blessington saw varied. There was kind Mrs Green, who was so grateful for the treatment she received on her home visit that once she was able to get out and about she called at the surgery with her dog, and left the doctor a bag of gooseberries.

A tall Jamaican man was sent to the treatment room after his appointment with Dr Blessington. When he arrived in the room I could see the young man was not happy because he had not been given a prescription on request. As a new patient he had been given an appointment – he was not a known patient, having just moved into the area. After consulting with him the doctor discovered this new patient was clearly dependent on illegal drugs. I spent a few minutes trying in vain to reason with this very agitated man, then he dashed out of the treatment room and headed back down the corridor towards Dr Blessington's room, with me hot on his heels followed by Pauline who was our practice manager at the time. Having been informed by the clerical staff that the patient was on his way back down to see him, Dr Bressington came out of his room just as the young man came face to face with him in the corridor. Words were exchanged then without warning the man lashed out to strike the doctor. The doctor's quick reactions made him duck, unfortunately for Pauline the blow missed the good doctor and hit her instead. Although startled, the practice manager was not hurt. The offender, who was shocked at hitting a woman, left abruptly, never to return.

Both patients and staff adored Dr Blessington who, in his quiet way, had a great sense of humour. This made him the choice person to play pranks on, so that's exactly what we did and I have to admit I was the world's worst for instigating most of them. One day, knowing that he was not over-fond of small creatures such as mice, I brought in a life-like toy mouse and while taking a patient's blood pressure I asked the lady in question if she would play along with me while I carried out a prank on Dr Blessington.

Having had the lady's consent I placed the mouse behind the leg of the examination couch and went to Dr Blessington room where I knocked, but opened his door before he could answer. I anxiously asked him if he would come to the treatment room quickly. Thinking there was an emergency Dr Blessington left the secretary he was dictating to and rushed to the treatment room. On entering the room he automatically went to check on the lady, who had just had her blood pressure checked.

'No! Not the patient,' I said.

'It's there!' and I pointed to the mouse.

On seeing the creature the doctor's face was a picture, and for a few seconds he froze then suddenly being aware of the patient's presence he looked around before grabbing the nearest thing, which happened to be the glass dressing trolley, and rammed the leg of the couch, throwing the mouse, dressings and implements up in the air.

By this time both the patient and I were helpless laughing. He turned in astonishment to me and with a firm tone said, 'I'll deal with you later.'

Then he marched back to his room to complete his dictations a little surprised but relieved that the creature was not real. He never did 'deal with me later.'

Then there was the time a delivery arrived for the treatment room in a 6-foot-long narrow box – just large enough for a body. Straight away I had an idea. Rather than waste the opportunity I gathered some of the staff to help me into the box and transport me in the box to stand in the corridor outside Dr Blessington's room. A member of the staff then knocked the door saying there was a delivery for the doctor and asked if he wanted it before he called for his next patient.

Within a few moments Dr Blessington opened the door and, faced with such a strange gift suspiciously kicked the box, which came crashing to the floor causing the box to burst open to reveal a rather stunned nurse inside. The doctor, shocked in case I was hurt, shook his head as he bent to help me out of the box, said smugly, 'Well, it does serve you right.'

One day Frances, one of the secretaries in the practice, bought a hamster in a cage during her lunch hour. On returning to work she brought it into the surgery until home time, rather than leave it in her car for hours. So once again, on seeing the small animal, I could not resist the opportunity to 'get' Dr Blessington and made it my mission to persuade Frances that she would not get the sack if she lent me the new-found pet for the afternoon. She finally gave in to me and reluctantly handed over the cage; I took the cage and placed it on Dr Blessington's desk to await his arrival to commence his afternoon surgery.

Four o'clock saw Dr Blessington enter his room to start his evening surgery. In the meantime the majority of the staff including myself had sneaked up the corridor to listen outside his door, waiting for the doctor's reaction. For a few seconds there was silence before squeaky sound followed. At hearing this I peeped in the door to find Dr Blessington pushing the cage complete with hamster at arm's length through his adjoining door, onto his partner's couch in the next room. Unfortunately his partner had started his early surgery and was in the middle of examining a patient on his couch at the time, and to the shock of both him and his patient Dr Blessington was trying to place the cage on the surprised patient's head.

The sight of the chaos caused by such a small hamster, and knowing that we helped instigate it, was enough to make me return to the treatment room followed by a hasty retreat of all members of staff to their posts. Adding to the chaos the hungry hamster had left his mark by chewing the doctor's immaculate desk pad through the bars of its cage while it waited on Dr Blessington's desk prior to his afternoon surgery.

Frances, who was relieved not to get fired after her hamster's visit to the surgery, was taking shorthand for Dr Blessington one afternoon. On many previous occasions she had experienced the doctor's quick sense of humour and this afternoon, while he was dictating his letters, was no different. As he hesitated during the dictation and tried to remember a patient's name Frances tried to jog his memory by recalling various names of patients he had seen recently, before she said, 'Does it ring any bells?'

'No that's Dr Kyd's phone next door,' was his quick reply.

Later Frances, although a little reluctantly, decided not only to move on but to move out of the country to go and live in Greece with her husband. He had previously taken an opportunity to go and work in Saudi Arabia, where after a time he had made his fortune, or at least enough to persuade Frances to sell up and emigrate for a new lifestyle. And it was while she was clearing her house in Riverdale that Frances gave me the gift of her slow cooker which she no longer required. This was useful because in those days within the practice the doctors held a routine business meeting at lunchtime on a Friday once a month, where often instead of having sandwiches brought in, Frances's slow cooker would come in handy, especially in the winter months when I was able on occasions to bring in a hot casserole or suchlike which was much appreciated and quickly devoured, giving the meeting a good start.

On Christmas Eve the little pot went down a treat as it kept my non-alcoholic mulled wine warm until the end of the morning surgery when the staff would gather in the reception area to share a buffet lunch that everyone had contributed to, providing a tasty table. Even if the now empty waiting room did smell more like a brewery after the wine had been left bubbling for a few hours, it did make a change from the odd smell of ether or surgical spirit drifting from the treatment room. Any unwanted smells were soon tackled that same afternoon, by our surgery cleaners, before closing the surgery for Christmas.

As for Frances, after a short spell of living in Greece she re-turned to her home town of Manchester. We missed her, especially if ever a hamster was mentioned, and often gave her a thought, especially her colleague Pauline who had shared the same office.

13

'Live Telegram'

Pauline had been employed at the surgery as a medical secretary after coming from the *Shropshire Star* (the local newspaper) where she had been the editor's personal secretary. She was so efficient at her job within the practice that she was soon promoted to practice manager, a new position where she not only managed the business side of the surgery but also the running of the practice commitments, one of which was geographically organising the doctors on their home visits to prevent them overlapping each other in different practice areas, in an attempt to save them and the patient time. Pauline was popular with the staff she worked with; this created a pleasant atmosphere within the workplace which was reflected back on the patients when they attended the reception desk, where they were greeted with a friendly encounter.

To the staff Pauline was a good manager, very approachable and fair between the members of those she managed: she always listened to their point of view or took on board any suggestions they might offer to improve the way the practice was run.

To the doctors who employed her she was a good secretary and practice manager, and an asset to the business side of the practice.

To me she was a dear friend who had attended our wedding with her first husband who had been Keith's best man. Our sons, who were the same age, both went to nursery then to school together, and Pauline and I had shared many an exhausting children's party where we tried to keep a number of toddlers amused for a few hours. The venues for these parties varied each year from a rowdy do at McDonald's 'golden arches' to a fairly sedate ride in a fancy cart pulled by a fine horse which was led by Billy, a local character of Jackend who also was the maker of the cart and the owner of the horse. He kept the children interested in the sights and things that they encountered before they reached their destination, which was my garden where they enjoyed the usual children's delights such as jelly and ice cream, and a piece of what was the latest attempt of an original up-to-date themed birthday cake; it was always satisfying when the children at least recognised what the cake was suppose to be.

One year we hired The Old Folks' Rest Room in Bendigo minus the old folk. We thought this would be a great place – space-wise it would allow the little rascals to run wild. That was, until they discovered there was a stage at the one end of the room, where unforeseen by Pauline or myself it proved to be a little too high for the three- and four-year olds to fall off safely. Nevertheless we survived yet another party.

To the staff Pauline was a colleague with a great sense of humour. She was attractive and fashionable, with a lovely smile, and was always ready for fun. One year Pauline and her son went on holiday to Spain with her mum and dad: they were staying in an apartment which had a sun terrace on the flat roof. Now Pauline and her mum had the type of skin that tanned easily in the sun whereas her dad (who had a fair skin and was more of a redhead) did not.

One day during the holiday Pauline, her mum and son went out for the day, locking up the apartment of course as they left. When they eventually returned many hours later they were shocked to discover they had accidentally locked her dad on the hot flat roof which had no shelter from the sun's powerful rays. He had been quietly reading in the shade of the morning when they left earlier in the day, and by the time they returned there was no escape from the heat, so when they found him he was dancing up and down trying to avoid the intense heat penetrating on his bare feet from the red-hot concrete, which made him look like a cooked lobster. Both ladies had to contain their laughter at the sight they saw, or risk being lynched by the not too happy man.

'Not easy,' said Pauline, when she related the tale to us two weeks later on her return to work.

Pauline was our first practice manager and very popular with the staff she managed, so it was inevitable that when she was getting married for the second time, having invited both the medical and clerical staff of the surgery to her special day, we all knew we had to give her a wedding event to remember. So we decided to organise a surprise telegram to be delivered on the day, to send her off into her new marriage in style.

Once we had received our invitations and knew what hotel the reception was to be held at, we contacted the manager to find out whether or not the hotel had a piano, and if so whether we would be allowed to make use of it at the reception. To our delight the manager informed us that there was a piano available for our use.

The next thing we had to set about doing was to make the costumes that we would change into and decide what we would sing while we delivered our 'live telegram'. Dr Blessington agreed to play the piano as long as he did not have to dress up.

As expected, Pauline made a lovely bride and the day was going well until the best man started to read the cards and telegrams. It had been previously arranged that during this time the surgery staff would discreetly leave the room to dress up quickly in preparation for their grand entrance when the best man introduced us. We took our leave from our various individual tables scattered around the room, leaving our husbands, wives and partners trying to look natural while the other guests puzzled as to what was going on. At the same time the bride and groom sitting at the top table were wondering why we all needed the toilet at the same time.

Once we were out of the room, we helped each other dress up as angels complete with wings and halos made out of coat hangers and fixed to the back of our heads. Then at the given time the best man announced to the wedding party that there was one more telegram which would be delivered in person. At hearing this we danced in singing to the tune of 'When the Saints Go Marching In', but instead of the original words we added our own version to the tune, words that were based around the life of the bride and groom.

The 'live telegram' completely surprised Pauline and Ken (her new husband) and caused a great deal of laughter amongst the guests, all except the bride's mother; her face showed her disapproval at some of the words of the song, probably because they revealed some dark secrets that the new mother-in-law did not want the other guests to know, and the inevitable jokes about mother-in-laws that were flying around did not help.

The sight of us standing around the piano, which Dr Blessington was trying to hide behind, was a picture in itself. We were all shapes and sizes with not much of a tune between us and looking more like devils than angels, emphasised by the sight of Dr Cummingham's halo which had slipped as he walked into the room and was left hanging over his ear of which he was totally unaware. This made it all the funnier.

Some years later the surgery staff attended the same venue when we were invited to Alma and Paul's wedding; Alma was one of the practice nurses employed in 1990 at the surgery. The fact that we actually received wedding invitation was a wonder, especially after the trick I played on her at work prior to her big day. The last week before the wedding arrived, and I could not resist grasping the opportunity to play some sort of joke on Alma, who had a rather shy personality. After giving it some thought I decided to contact the local bobbies who at the time had their police station at the bottom of The Brae in Bendigo.

The easiest thing was to ring the police station and persuade the policeman who answered the phone that if he would send an officer to arrest one of our nurses in the name of fun, it would be a good gesture and might help with community relations. He in turn exhausted himself telling me all the reasons why he could not send policemen to waste time acting the fool while on duty, then finally gave in and agreed.

Alma turned up for work as normal eager to get through her last day before her holiday, and as she came through the surgery door she was more than a little surprised to be faced with a huge banner draped across the waiting room wall. The banner, which had been prepared by the staff, advertised to the patients that Alma was getting married and congratulated her, wishing her the best on her big day. Alma's reaction was to hurry past the streamers and balloons that decorated the rest of the room, and take refuge in the treatment room.

Later, just before lunchtime, two police officers arrived at the reception desk and asked if Alma could be called to the waiting room to be interviewed. The receptionist telephoned the treatment room and asked Alma to present herself as quickly as possible to the desk. The baffled Alma rushed out of the treatment room and came face to face with the officers of the law, who asked her to confirm who she was before starting to say she had committed a traffic violation. But before they could finish, Alma burst out laughing and said, 'This is a hoax, it's not real.'

Realising she was not going to take the situation seriously, the policemen joined in with the rest of the staff including the doctors who had just finished their appointments, and had gathered to have photographs taken to mark the occasion.

The rest of the day was not without its moments of fun, giving Alma a few fond memories of her last working day as a Miss before she tied the knot; having played several tricks on our bride-to-be while she was at work we planned to behave ourselves when we were guests at her wedding, so there was no live telegram repeated.

However, when help was wanted within the practice the staff never hesitated to do whatever was necessary, no matter what it might be, and all the better if the help that was needed was arranging some event or other. Another occasion some time later was when we all pulled together in order to help yet another of our female practice managers organise her wedding reception.

The excitement of the special day could be felt from early morning with all hands on deck as we arrived at the venue for the reception, which was to be held in the village hall in Shotts. Here, together with the bride's family, we transformed the room with the help of the staff members who were gifted with being artistic, while the others showed off their talent in preparing a banquet fit for a king. Then we all dashed home, titivated ourselves up and after we had attended the lovely wedding ceremony which took place in a church outside Rosebank we travelled back to Shotts to spend the rest of the afternoon and evening enjoying a great party.

Finally as a surprise for the bride and groom I organised a week's honeymoon in York. Because the couple had not budgeted enough for a holiday I approached a patient who had offered me in the past (as a thank you) the use of her deluxe caravan. Thanks to this patient the bride and groom were able to have the accommodation for the week after their wedding.

The newly-weds gladly accepted the holiday. But it came to an abrupt end midway through the week when another family arrived on the doorstep of the caravan, having been mistakenly double booked by the owner for the same week. Fortunately everyone involved saw the funny side of it all: in actual fact the newlyweds had enough of caravanning and were only too keen to get back to Rosebank where they had a lot to do to settle into their new home. After the excitement of the wedding the staff settled back down to work by carrying out their normal daily duties, a lot of which included attending to the requests of the practice population and their need to be seen. The next routine fun involvement that the practice expected to engage in was still a few months ahead – Christmas.

The months seemed to fly past and it seemed like no time before it was the first week of December and the buzz of the anticipation of Christmas was already in the air. I was frequently asked by many of the patients that had appointments to see me, 'Are you already for Christmas, Nurse?'

So it was of no surprise when Mr Porter arrived for his appointment and asked the same thing.

'Not quite ready yet,' I answered.

He looked pleased with himself as he told me, 'Well, my wife and I are all organised. She has cooked and plated the Christmas dinner and put it in the freezer, so we just have to take it out and microwave it on the big day.'

Now that was what I call being prepared, but could Christmas really be Christmas without the smell of Brussels sprouts being cooked on the actual day?

Perhaps Mr Porter, who made an appointment to tell me the same thing every year, did not like the smell of Brussels sprouts and unlike most had found a remedy to avoid the odour while opening his Christmas presents, an exercise I presume that was left until Christmas Day.

One Christmas Bendigo Ladies' Circle decided that it would be good if their members could take some of Bendigo children who had never been to a pantomime to see one. It was agreed that the ladies in Circle would come up with a list of children they knew who would like to be taken to the pantomime, the nearest of which was at Wolverhampton Theatre.

Off duty, as an active member of the Bendigo Ladies Circle I tried where possible to ensure that the charity funds received were returned back into the community from which they had come, by applying it to deliver care and to benefit those who needed it most. If any child deserved such an outing Jack did.

Now, Jack was a seven-year-old asthmatic boy who came to see me every week for his check-up which included measuring him to check on his growth (he was small for his age). He would stand as straight as he could against the measuring tape on the wall, waiting with anticipation to hear me say he had grown since last week. Jack was very self-conscious about his height as he was one of the smallest in his class at school. The medication he had received in the past was believed to have had the side-effect of affecting his growth, although when I asked him if he wanted to go to the theatre and would he ask his mum if I could take him, he stood tall with pride.

It was the night of the theatre trip and Jack arrived at the surgery in his little gaberdine coat with a shining clean face, and we set off with a coach full of excited children who joined in singing and laughing all the way to Wolverhampton. Once we were in the theatre the children seemed more delighted with the novelty of going back and forward to the toilets in the theatre than sitting still in their seats to watch the pantomime, while the other members of the Ladies' Circle and myself just spent the night taking it in turn chaperoning the children back and forth to the loo, seeing very little of the show that night.

However, once the pantomime was finished and we had counted all the children onto the coach we were pleased to deliver the very thrilled and very tired children safely back to their parents who were waiting their arrival at Bendigo. Some years later Jack, now a tall young man, called into the surgery to see me, and during his visit he reminded me of his theatre trip when he was little and just how much it had meant to him.

Christmas at the practice was an event that every one of the staff looked forward to. Weeks before Christmas Eve we would decide what theme to have, then everyone would set to and make, borrow or buy their dressing-up outfit. No one particularly wanted the day off, instead we would all bring in a variety of food and soft drinks to display a bountiful buffet. All staff including those on the community, district nurses, health visitors and medical reps would be invited to drop in.

The patients would call in to the surgery on Christmas Eve for no other reason than just to see the staff dressed up in their outfits, and the adults would bring along the children to have a look. Over the years characters ranged from Mother Christmas to Minnie Mouse. The Minnie Mouse idea had come from me having just been to Florida for a holiday, and as it was the most original theme I could think of with the little time I had to plan it. One of the best outfits I remember appeared on one Christmas when everyone had made a great effort to make their costumes, and dressed as something from the Christmas tree. Shirley was a cracker and could hardly walk, wrapped in a large tube: the practice manager was the fairy from the top of the tree: one receptionist was a snowman wearing a top hat: another was the tree itself with flowing branches: and another was Mother Christmas.

One year Keith, Craig and I had booked to go on a Christmas holiday with Margaret and Bill. The idea of going to see our cousin who lived in Jamaica had come from Margaret earlier on in the year, to give us time to think about it and save to do so. Before we left on our Christmas holiday I joined the surgery staff who had booked a Christmas meal at a local venue where we could share in the festive cheer together, carrying on the tradition of fancy dress since all the staff members would not be present at the practice on Christmas Eve. The theme that evening was that of The Muppets with the receptionists dressed as Miss Piggy, Kermit the Frog and an old man with a safety pin through his head. I don't quite know who he was meant to be, but I do know that the safety pin did its rounds that night, while the cameras clicked all night.

Another fun night the surgery staff entered into full-heartedly was a Murder Mystery where the venue was at the Bowls Hotel just up the road on the Muir Hill beyond Jackend. During the week prior to the night out each member of staff was given a character to imitate, drawn out of a hat. My character was to be the Black Widow and my imagination went wild as I set to putting my outfit together. The effect paid off when three members of staff arrived with Dr Cummingham who had offered to pick me up.

In the night the car's headlights caught my dark figure, dressed in a flowing black gown. On my head was a black bonnet which tied under my chin, with a black veil covering my face. I walked slowly towards the car with my head hung low, carrying a single white lily held with hands wearing black lace gloves. My appearance made the passengers in the car gasp with fright before they dissolved into laughter, to which I pretended to weep, acting out my character role.

During our meal the hotel staff provided us with clues about the murder, and I howled and sobbed every time my poor dead husband was mentioned in the tale. At the end of the meal the murder mystery was solved and a member of staff gained a prize from the hotel. The manager presented me with a tot of brandy (which I passed to a colleague) as a prize for my acting, although I think secretly he was trying to shut me up.

It was certainly an evening with a difference, and one that we all thought we might be able to repeat some time in the future, but never did.

14

Accidents do Happen

The fifth partner, Dr Gardener, was an expert when it came to paediatric care and he certainly had a way with children that put them at ease when they entered his consulting room; this was not always an easy task when one is dealing with a frightened child in pain. Part of the doctor's skills may have been attributed to the fact that he had young children of his own at the time and found it easy to relate to his patients about the latest children's TV programme or toy character just out. He was always a favourite when it came to antenatal care, and his clinics were always fully booked mainly because of his understanding and caring attitude; an antenatal lady once described him as a Greek God because of his fair hair and handsome looks, as she put it.

His staff respected him and thought of him as being a good doctor with a quiet nature. They found him approachable when they went to him regarding any problems that arose within the running of the practice; however he could also be assertive when dealing with his staff: if he said no for any reason, he meant no.

He was not without his sense of humour. One day while he was in surgery he was consulting with a patient who had black hair apart from a thick white streak of hair that dominated the front of his forehead like a lightning streak.

'I see you are a Mallon,' smiled the doctor.

'Ho! No, I am a Finigan from the dump,' replied the patient.

At that time there was a popular well-known series on television called the Mallon Streak in which the family in the series all had a trademark white streak of hair on their forehead.

One very wet morning Dr Gardener was in the reception area collecting his patients' records (before computers were in use), in preparation to see his appointments booked when Mabel the practice nurse arrived for work. Now Mabel travelled from her home in Tully to Bendigo by means of her pride and joy – a motorbike; and as a very practical person she owned all the gear that was required for her powerful transport. But on this particular morning she was not happy, and never did hide the fact that things did not please her at times, so she stormed into reception dressed in her black leathers, very wet and slippery, chewing about some car driver that had tried to cut her up at the traffic lights.

As a rule when Mabel was mad about anything the rest of the staff would normally keep out of her road until she calmed down, but on this morning they had gathered around to listen to her grumble; and grumble she did, at the same time as taking off her outdoor clothes. It was when she removed her crash helmet that she revealed a newly hand-knitted balaclava, now steaming with vapours of sweat caused by her hot head – not too surprising because she did have lovely long thick hair under it. The picture of Mabel in this state was too much for the staff to bear and they collapsed into laughter, but not as much as Dr Gardener who quickly took his records and disappeared into his room to try and compose himself before calling his first patient through.

Dr Gardener was also a favourite with the elderly, and as part of his weekly routine duties he would attend to the elderly residents who were registered as our patients at the Tinto Hospital. This was usually an early visit before surgery hours, and on some mornings the old ladies would present him with the odd thank you in the form of a flower from the vase on their bedside locker, which he sometimes brought back to the surgery and left in the reception area as he passed by on his way to his room to start his morning appointments.

Another favourite with the senior patients was the new partner Dr Moil. It was a great asset to the practice when Dr Moil (known by us as Dr Mo) joined as a partner back in 1981. He proved such a caring and likeable person, and nothing was ever too much trouble to him. This made working with him a pleasure, and his manner to patients and his colleagues was always impeccable. He was one of the few doctors I know who would stand up as a patient entered his consulting room and would open the door for them, shaking their hand as they left.

Very often when he was on call at night he had been known to arrive at the patient's home still wearing his pyjama top under his jacket, a sign of how quickly he had rushed to get to them, and although this was noticed by the patient and their families they appreciated his dedication to them.

Part of Dr Mo's surgery duty was to care for the soldiers and their families based at the garrison camp. There, on several occasions, I had been called upon to give talks to the ladies of 15 Battalion in the Army, to show them different methods of contraception, accompanied by a theory-based talk, hopefully in an attempt to increase their awareness and to update their knowledge on aspects of preconception advice, contraception, family planning and cytology screening, including current research findings. The aim was to encourage the group of soldiers to be motivated to assess their own needs without fear, and take responsibility for their own bodies, because many of the female soldiers were known for failing to attend for their smear tests and other routine health checks, mainly because of inconvenience due to their duties.

This then led on to the service that provided antenatal care for the soldiers' wives when necessary. This was in the form of a clinic held in the camp each week, when Dr Mo and myself would attend.

It was after such a clinic one Tuesday that Dr Mo was giving me a lift back to the Boweryhill Surgery in his Suzuki jeep and decided he wanted me to hear his latest music tape. After groping among his many tapes he found the appropriate one and played its chanting music: this was done as we travelled along.

So intent was he on the new music that we automatically followed the bus that was travelling in front of us from Daisywood into the bus lay-by at Bendigo in front of the surgery.

'Mind the bus,' I called as the bus came to a halt.

'What bus?' he said.

'The one in front of us!' I replied, just as we bumped into it.

The irate driver jumped out of his seat and flew at us. 'What are you doing?' he yelled.

'Sorry,' said the startled Dr Mo.

The damage to the jeep was not noticed much: because there were so many bumps and dents all over it, it just blended in; even the roof had not escaped a dent or two and in fact the staff used to say it looked like a domino. Thankfully however the bus appeared to be unscratched, so we managed to creep sheepishly away from the bus driver back to the surgery. 'What do you think of the tape?' Dr Mo grinned, as he held the surgery door open for me.

I was too stunned to answer; he had been so pleased with his new tune that he was totally unaware of the hazardous drive we had just had.

Having an adventurous drive with Dr Mo was not really unusual. One day after work Dr Mo drove another practice nurse (Mabel) and myself to a study evening which was funded by one of the medical companies that supplied the surgery; the venue for the study was held at the Western Park House. On entering this grand house the guests were each handed a glass of Buck's Fizz, which was topped up now and again as we wondered around this lovely building being given a guided tour prior to the lecture, which was followed by dinner.

Unknown to Mabel and me Dr Mo was not aware that the Buck's Fizz contained alcohol. Then we heard him say to the waitress as she served the wine, 'No, thank you, I don't drink wine but I would like some more of that nice orange juice we had on arrival.'

The waitress without hesitation returned with a bottle of Buck's Fizz, much to the delight of Dr Mo, the effects of which we were soon about to discover after the evening ended as we drove through the grounds of Western Park on our way home. I said to our dear driver, 'Dr Mo, can you see that grey line over there?'

'Yes,' he replied.

'Well that is the road. We are on the grass.'

However with a little help from his passengers Dr Moil got us home safely without causing any accidents.

Although no one is immune from accidents some mishaps can in some cases turn out to be quite funny, as I was reminded one day when I was travelling in the car during one of my frequent visits to Ireland. The car radio was on and I was listening to the local news, and the newsreader was relating an accident that had occurred earlier that day.

'There has been an accident on the Tullamore Road,' announced the newsreader, 'where a motor cyclist has been knocked down. The accident happened because a cow got onto the road and into the path of the cyclist. The cyclist sustained only minor injuries. The cow has been taken into custody until the owner comes forward.'

Hearing this news my imagination conjured up a large heifer in a small cell with only a bench to lie on while she awaited her fate.

Following another few items of interest the newsreader continued, giving out the latest funeral information that was to take place that day: 'The sudden death has occurred of Mike O'Brian yesterday. He fell from his ladder from a height of twenty feet. But it was not the fall that caused his death. It was him hitting his head on the scaffolding as he got up that did it.'

The Irish definitely tell it as it is. At least the man who called to put up Craig's television aerial did when I mentioned to him that it was a good thing he was not afraid of heights. He was climbing up his ladder onto the roof of the house carrying equipment in both hands, the sight of which made me nervous, probably more so because I don't like heights. When he came indoors to check the effects of the aerial on the television screen, I told him I could not do his job because I did not like heights.

'Neither do I,' he said.

'Really?' I queried.

'Especially after I fell.'

'What happened?'

'Well you see, I was on the roof of a single-storey house.'

'Was it a bungalow?'

He nodded and continued, 'And like today I was holding something in both my hands when I slipped and fell.'

'Were you badly hurt?'

'No, very shocked. You see I landed on my feet like a cat. There I stood for a few moments still holding the things in my hands. When my boss came around the corner and told me to stop hanging about and get on with the job. Well I could not speak, never mind move. That's as much sympathy you get in this job.'

'It hasn't put you off doing this work?' I replied.

'No, but I have not fallen off a house roof yet,' he grinned.

Of course accidents all too often have their darker sides, and this was what happened to my grandfather as long ago as 1912. He was a slater by trade and was employed by Mr Lithgow, Slater & Plasterer. It was Saturday 19th May, and the Caledonian Hotel in Lanark was undergoing external redecoration. In the morning Mr Murphy, a painter, was up his ladder engaged in painting the front of the hotel. He was close to the rain pipe which he took hold of to steady himself while on the ladder.

A portion of the pipe about 6 feet in length came away without warning, and knocked Mr Murphy from his ladder, causing him to fall a distance of 30 feet. A local GP, Dr Kelly, was called to attend to him and the doctor did not hesitate to have the injured man transferred to St Mary's Hospital in Lanark, where he was diagnosed to have sustained injury to his spine causing slight paralysis: he was also suffering from concussion and shock.

Later in the afternoon my grandfather with another colleague,

Slater, were called to replace the portion of the rain pipe that had fallen; the men mounted separate ladders and proceeded to replace the pipe. The ladder Grandfather was on slipped on the newly painted wall and fell, bringing Grandfather along with it; unfortunately his head hit the pavement first, in almost the same spot as Mr Murphy had fallen earlier in the day. He was picked up unconscious and carried into the hotel where he was seen by Dr Guthrie, another GP, who speedily had him taken to the Lockhart Hospital, although there was little hope of recovery: his injuries included a fractured skull and brain damage.

Late in the afternoon an operation was performed but proved of no avail, as Grandfather died the following morning. He was only 37 years old and left behind his wife and ten children, the youngest of which was not 12 months old. Grandmother received widespread sympathy as such an accident had shocked the town. The fact that grandfather was well-known throughout the town, and had enjoyed the respect of all classes, became obvious at his funeral which was a public one attended by a large number of mourners. As the cortege slowly wound its way to the churchyard there were many signs of respect paid to him by the numerous sympathising onlookers, while the majority of the places of business were temporarily closed; other tradesmen and co-workers sent several wreaths.

Mr Murphy the painter died from his injuries in St Mary's Hospital four days after the accident; this was also a funeral that was well attended.

15

Birthday Surprises

In an attempt to bring some fun into the practice we (the staff) would use any excuse to have a party; usually it would be a special birthday. Such an event took place when it was Dr Daffin's fiftieth birthday when, unknown to him, I bought a batch of birthday cards and packets of balloons, and after getting the staff to help blow up the balloons I arranged for a balloon and a birthday card to be given to each of the patients with an appointment to see Dr Daffin that morning, so they could sign the card before presenting it along with a balloon to the doctor as they entered his room for their consultation.

Midway through his morning surgery Dr Daffin rang the reception desk to say he could not move in his room for balloons. At this point he was asked if he would come down to the reception to sign a prescription that was urgently needed. To his embarrassment, when he arrived at the desk, we had arranged for an attractive young lady dressed as a belly dancer (who just happened to be the next patient booked to see him) to dance for him in front of a full waiting room of delighted patients, before she gave him a hand to cut his birthday cake that his dear wife had baked. Dr Daffin knew how to enter into the spirit of things and took it all in his stride.

As he did with his patients. One day he was called out on a home visit to a new patient who lived in a flat, and when the doctor entered the building he was met with an agitated lady standing at the door of her flat

'Here you are at last, the trouble is over here.' She pointed to the kitchen and stood back to let the doctor through before following. 'It won't switch on,' she said, standing in front of the cooker

Dr Daffin, being the helpful man he was, poked around the cooker. Unable to find a solution to the problem he glanced at his watch and, realising he had better make a move and get on with his own work, he apologised.

'Sorry but I think you will have to get someone to look at the cooker. Now, let me have a look at you. What is your trouble?'

'Why? Who are you?'

'I am Dr Daffin.'

'I thought you were the gas man,' said the surprised lady.

Another surprised lady was Anne (one of the receptionists) who would go all weak at the knees when a certain young man came in for an appointment. Knowing how she felt about him, one day when the young man came into the treatment room I asked if he would oblige by doing me a favour. Thinking it might affect the way he was treated he thought he had better not refuse, so agreed, asking what it might be. I told the young man that Anne's twenty first birthday was in a few days and asked him if he would bring her in a rose, which I would provide for him. Feeling he had to oblige, and after sorting out times, he agreed and left.

On the day of Anne's birthday there was the usual display of banners along with the merriment that warranted such a morning but, unknown to Anne, all members of the staff were secretly keeping an eye out for the young man due to arrive around 11 a.m. Sure enough at the given time there was a gasp of excitement and the reception staff gathered around the window to see the young man walking through the streets of Bendigo. He was dressed in his dinner jacket and bow tie, carrying at shoulder height a silver tray with a red rose and a glass of champagne on it. He looked just like the man on the TV advert at the time when Martini was being promoted as the 'in' drink to have.

Like a true gentleman he entered the surgery and, after kissing the shocked but thrilled birthday girl, he presented her with the flower and glass of bubbly. In the months that followed, the same young man went on to become a professional snooker player.

They say life begins at 40, so I did expect something to happen when I reached the grand old age, but it was still a surprise on the day itself when I had a telephone call (while I was in the middle of a busy child vaccination clinic) telling me that Dr Cummingham wanted to see me at once.

'But I am in the midst of a clinic,' I protested.

'He wants to see you now,' claimed the receptionist.

Without any further delay I completed the task in hand, which was giving a baby her first vaccine, before I headed over to the reception area to see what the urgency was. To my shock I found Dr Cummingham who was waiting at the reception desk, and only then did it dawn on me that the urgency was my birthday surprise. He stood there with a grin on his face as he presented me with a bottle of champagne and a prescription with instructions to be taken three times a day.

Then to my astonishment a handsome young man came in the surgery door dressed as Tarzan, wearing only a skimpy loincloth and with a toy monkey tied to his right leg, and carrying a red rose between his teeth. He started to chase me around the waiting room, much to the delight of the mums and babies sitting there.

This was the start of what proved to be a week of events I will not forget. When I got home from work the doorbell never stopped ringing with friends and neighbours calling with gifts and cards wishing me a happy birthday. Then later that same evening Keith took me out for dinner, which turned out to be a surprise party with all those friends present that had already called at the house beforehand as a ploy to throw me off the scent. Thinking that a party was inevitable I enjoyed the evening, so it came as a total shock when the following night a 53-seat coach pulled up at the bottom of our drive and whisked me off towards Minton to what I discovered later was a 'This is Your Life' party.

The coach was full of relatives and friends who had come from Scotland, London and locally, although I was not aware of who was on the coach, because when I got on I was made to sit in the front seat and was not allowed to look back. Whenever I tried to see who was sitting at the back I was distracted by Dr Daffin and his wife who were in the seat behind me and who had been given the job of keeping my attention away from the guests who were hiding behind the seats in the back of the bus.

The 90 people present that evening enjoyed a wonderful entertaining party when after the food was served Helen and Margaret put on a show. It started with my sisters doing a double act and telling a story, beginning with Helen producing a doll fully clothed from beneath the bin bag that she was wearing and promptly dropped it on the floor, landing on its head. This was to illustrate my birth, although I have never delivered a baby fully dressed and nor has anyone else. Helen carried out the acting well while Margaret told the tale which she read from the red book in the form of a poem:

The war had just been ended
The battle had been won
The forces were just returning home
And they deserved some fun

The wives they were awaiting
Ready to receive their men
So begins my story
'Are you ready to hear it, hen?'

Some forty years ago from now
And the May blossom was still in bud
A wee bairn was born to Mr & Mrs Dickie
And landed with such a thud

She was such a bonnie wee thing
Her two brothers and three sisters did agree
Richard said, 'Oh but another lassie.'
Said Helen, 'Good, she'll be under me.'

They all crept about the house for a while
To give the bairn peace
But in the middle of the night when they all wanted sleep
They wished her bawling would cease

Then in the morning when she would coo and laugh
They would forget the night before
They would all join in and play with her
And roll around the floor

Soon summer passed to autumn
The winter chill drew nigh
And in the year of 1945 they little knew
Their father would die

The happy home was soon disturbed
Not by the bairn at all
The good Lord needed her father
And to him He gave the call

She was only a few months old and to all
The blow was ever so hard
Her mum had lost a good husband
And the children they missed their dad

John had to join the Navy
Nancy had to leave home as well
The rest of them had some growing to do
And all a story could tell

Throughout the night, as the story was told, different members of my family appeared at the given moment. These were the guests that had been hiding behind the seats on the bus and had kept out of sight in the bar until being beckoned to play their part in the cabaret, which for me came as a great surprise. After such a wonderful evening the last thing I expected the following morning was to have a chauffer-driven Rolls-Royce pull up to my front door to take me off to lunch with my sisters, who were already in the car. We were driven through Rosebank, waving to the passers-by on the way until we reached our destination, the Meadow Hotel in Build was where we indulged in an exotic lunch. Then to complete the day, once again a coach arrived at our house that evening and took me to another party: chicken and chips and a disco at the Station Pub at Haybride. Life beginning at 40 certainly had a lot more in store.

Birthday surprises were not only a tradition of the practice, they were also a regular occurrence in the Dickie family when a member reached special landmarks in life. Such was the case the day before our Richard's sixtieth birthday when we four sisters, Nancy, Helen, Margaret and myself, travelled with Bill and Jack my brothers-in-law from Shropshire to Scotland, intending to surprise Richard the following night at a restaurant in Lanark where his family had booked a birthday meal for him.

Margaret, Bill, Helen and Jack had booked their accommodation on the outskirts of Lanark so once they had checked in, and after Nancy and I had booked into our accommodation in Lanark, we all visited my brother John and his wife Jean that evening to arrange the plans for the birthday party. However the evening took an unexpected twist when pride came before a fall.

Nancy and I were boasting in fun to the others how much better our accommodation was compared to theirs with their brown bathroom suite which had an unusual bath, designed with an indentation of a seat in the middle. The shape of the seat formed that of a pair of buttocks, so Helen and Margaret decided they wanted to come and see for themselves and insisted I showed them our upmarket bed and breakfast just up the road from John's home.

We left John's apartment and as Helen was descending the first set of stairs that led to his flat she fell, injuring her leg. Going to her aid we found she was unable to weight bear on her one ankle: there was no other option but to get her to a hospital to eliminate the possibility of any fracture she might have sustained.

The idea of seeing the posh accommodation went out the window as we hurried to take Helen to the nearest hospital which was 20 minutes' drive away. Without too much delay Helen was helped into the car, accompanied by her husband Jack in the back seat and our John to show us the way in the passenger seat next to me. As I drove off the snow started to fall, making our journey more hazardous in the dark. Eventually we reached the Law Hospital in Carluke. It was around 10 p.m. and even though it was a Friday night in Accident and Emergency, one of the busiest nights usually, Helen was attended to right away. There was a long wait for Helen's X-ray results, so long that John and I lost Jack in the Casualty unit and after searching for some time we found him in a cubicle behind a screen, stretched out on an examination couch.

'What are you doing, Jack?' questioned John.

'Oh I was just having a rest while I waited for Helen,' Jack yawned.

'You could be taken for a patient and goodness knows what they'll do to you,' said John.

Jack seemed unperturbed. He was feeling too tired as the effects of the long journey earlier in the day were taking their toll.

Eventually, Helen was discharged from the Casualty unit and came out of hospital about midnight, complete with a big white plaster on her injured leg where the X-rays had confirmed she had a fracture.

Having gotten over the trauma of the night before, the next evening we sisters arrived at the restaurant where Richard's birthday meal had been booked by his daughter Susan and her brother Wilson. Once at the table we quickly set to and decorated the room with banners and balloons, finishing just before the birthday boy was due to arrive. As Richard entered the full restaurant he did not notice us at first, then on catching sight of us was shocked but delighted that we were there. Then on seeing Helen's plastered leg he thought it was a wind-up and made an attempt to kick it in jest but was stopped by the roar that came from everyone as they shouted, 'Don't, it's real!'

The thought of yet another visit to the Law Hospital was too much to bear. Instead we all enjoyed a noisy but entertaining evening where other diners present in the restaurant sat back, pleased to have free entertainment laid on by members of the Dickie family.

After a lengthy evening of chatter and laughter during which we had all enjoyed a tasty meal washed down with perhaps too much wine, the family and friends made our way down the brae from Lanark to Richard's home in Kirkfieldbank where the party continued, with most members of the group doing their party piece throughout the rest of the evening. The entertainment took the form of a song, dance or funny story, a few of which Wilson was happy to oblige with. Helen's input to the entertainment, disabled as she was, came in the form of a poem she wrote, summing up Richard's life.

16

The Lad from the North

Then along came Kyd, the lad from the North born in Whitley Bay, Tyne and Wear; 'big Kyd', as he was known by the staff, was a 6 foot plus dark curly haired Dennis the Menace look-alike, and sometimes acted like him too, full of mischief. He was a young man full of enthusiasm and bursting with new ideas to enhance the practice, and at the same time hoped to increase the financial state of the surgery wherever possible by introducing changes that would help to do so. The day that Dr Killjoy was employed at the surgery was the start of the onset of changes within the surgery, some of which, no one could have foreseen.

The only problem, well perhaps not the only, but one of the problems with Kyd's sudden burst of dynamic energy was his overpowering manner with the patients, who up until now had taken things in their stride and were more familiar with the 'Old' GPs and their approach to them, and had got used to the treatments and medicines they had received in the past. Now they were suddenly treated by a young Geordie, as they called him, who armed with the latest and best medicine he had gained knowledge of hoped to cure the practice population in record time.

Now knowledge was the one thing Kyd was not short of. In the past he had won a scholarship to Clare College Cambridge and had gone on to improve his professional development, especially when it came to the latest research or topic that was newly discovered, when he would be keen to introduce it to his patients if he thought they would benefit from it. Getting patients to adapt to change was a little more difficult and sometimes took some persuasion, more so with the diabetic patients. As diabetes was one of Kyd's favourite subjects he soon brought about vast changes in the treatment of his diabetic patients compared with what they had received in the past.

Throughout my years as a practice nurse I saw many changes take place in medicine and have adapted to change easier through the various courses and study days and evenings I have attended in order to be up to date with the latest research. These, I feel, motivated me to encourage and introduce change within the surgery, to meet the patients' needs and to promote health. I remember going to an evening lecture along with other practice nurses from various GP practices in and around Shropshire to learn of the latest treatments for diabetics, presented to us by some of the best consultants and professors in the area, only to discover that we in our practice were already giving the latest advice and treatments to our patients and in some cases had been for some time, under Kyd's instructions.

The venues for such study evenings were usually funded by some drug company hoping to promote their latest product and held in a stately home or a fancy hotel with an additional bonus of an lavish meal and a good supply of wine after the lecture. During the meal our staff present on the evening could boast to the table guests next to them how our surgery already administered such new-found discoveries thanks to Kyd, and in some instances we were able to give some positive feedback as to the results of doing so.

At the beginning of Dr Killjoy's life at the surgery, his big problem appeared to be how to relate to the Bendigo patients registered at our surgery; his bedside manner, or lack of it, was one most of the patients had not come across before. This young GP was more matter of fact and did not waste time chatting: he would call a spade a spade and although he was usually right in what he said to them, he just had not got the older GPs' years of experience of how to deal with any fears of his patients, caused by having information that they may not have been able to cope with. Perhaps softening the edges as he addressed the patients' problems would have enabled them to accept things better. Kyd had his set ways, especially when it came to time-keeping: for example, if a patient had been given a ten-minute appointment they very rarely got 12 minutes with him. In the early days of becoming a GP he was so keen to keep to time with his appointments that he removed the two patients' chairs that were in his consulting room before his surgery started one day, and when one patient asked him where the chair was Dr Killjoy, who was sitting behind his desk, told the patient that there was no time for them to sit because he had a lot of people to see.

This was just a teething problem at the start and it only happened once. It was short-lived because when his colleagues and staff heard about it they soon put him wise that this was not the done thing in our practice. One patient who had an appointment with Kyd was rather irritated by the fact that the doctor was so intent on checking the computer notes that he appeared to ignore the patient sitting there in his room.

After a few moments of looking at the doctor the patient said, 'The only time you smile, Doctor, is when you've got the wind.'

Dr Killjoy reacted by bursting out laughing.

When it came to the social side of Kyd, he was a star. If there was a challenge when the staff were divided into teams against each other, because he was full of fun everyone wanted to be on his team. He was never short of ideas and could cheat like the best of us if he did not win. He usually, reluctantly, came second.

We had some great events such as the annual car treasure hunt, funded again by one of the medical companies. Sometimes the events of the night would be arranged by one of the company representatives who would provide the clues which we had to find on the way to the mysterious venue where we would eventually end up. We would discover when we got there who had given in by looking into the sealed envelope given to each team as they set off: the contents of the envelope, which were only to be opened as a last resort, told us where to meet in case we got lost.

The form for the evening would be to start from the surgery car park. The staff, who had been picked by their names being pulled out of a hat to decide which doctor's car they would be in, would work as a team and try and collect the items asked for on the list handed to them as they drove off.

Skittles, tenpin bowling, shooting with laser guns, and a visit to a Russian circus were but a few of the events that helped boost the staff morale over the years. We even had a day trip to Blackpool one Sunday when we hired a 52-seater coach to take the staff, along with their family or friends that wanted to come, for a blustery day on the beach before we took on the challenge of the fairground.

Although Kyd was daring he was not always the bravest person, and on that day he pushed me to sit with him at the front of the helter-skelter ride. When I protested that I did not like this sort of thing he replied neither did he but could not go on it on his own and had to take someone more afraid than him to make him feel better. Since his lovely wife was pregnant with their second child she had the excuse of having to looking after their small toddler who was enjoying the look on Daddy's face as she stood with Mummy watching the daredevil ride like any other sensible person.

Kyd had a good sense of humour, not surprising I suppose since he once told me his family background had Irish connections, and having visited Ireland several times I could appreciate the Irish sense of humour which comes naturally from all ages, especially the children who can be so comical.

One experience of the children's humour was when Keith and I spent our first Christmas in Ireland after Craig had gone there to live. Craig was renting a terraced house while his own house was being built, and we went to stay over the festive season. Craig was at work and Keith and I were in the kitchen when the front doorbell rang. As Keith opened the door he was greeted with three neighbouring children who had been playing in the road with a large frisbee: their aunt who lived in America had sent them it for Christmas.

'Can we have our frisbee back, mister?' said one boy, staring at Keith.

'It's blown over your roof into your back garden,' explained another boy.

'Just a moment,' said Keith.

He went through the hall to the kitchen to go and fetch the frisbee through the back door, only to find the door locked. He could not find where Craig kept the key, so going back to the front door he told the children, 'We can't open the back door at the moment, come back in a few minutes.'

The bewildered children stared at Keith before leaving. Less than five minutes later the doorbell rang again and when Keith opened the door there stood the three children.

'Can we have our frisbee back, now mister?' they echoed.

'Sorry, I still can't find the key,' apologised Keith. 'Give me a few more minutes,' he uttered as he closed the door.

We frantically looked for the key, in vain, then as we looked through the kitchen window we saw the neighbour from next door, still wearing her purple satin pyjamas, climbing over the fence which divided our gardens to retrieve the large American frisbee. Once again the doorbell rang and this time we both went to open the door, and to our surprise there stood the three children accompanied by their mother.

'Sorry, but my son has gone to work and we don't know where he keeps the back door key,' explained Keith.

'Oh, that's OK,' she said. 'You see, the children told me that Fred Elliot, the butcher from *Coronation Street*, was here on holiday and I had to come and see for myself,' she laughed.

'Well,' laughed Keith, 'I am not as bald as him.'

We all enjoyed the good humour and although the children were happy to get their frisbee back they were a little disappointed that they had not met the celebrity who they thought they could boast to their friends at school about after the Christmas holidays.

The following year in the spring we were visiting the grounds of one of the stately homes in Ireland and I was having a look around the garden nursery where there were some exotic plants for sale, when I heard some children calling to their mother.

'Where are you, Mammy?'

'I am here,' answered the young mother from behind a large

plant. 'We don't want to lose you,' said the daughter.

'We would have no one to girn in our faces if we lost you,' said her sister.

Hearing this I continued wandering around the plants, smiling to myself at the quick remarks that came off the cuff from these youngsters, when I saw an elderly couple looking at me in an odd way. Feeling I had to explain my stupid grin, I told them what I had heard.

'Well, really, some cheek these children have,' said the very Irish lady, shaking her head in disapproval at what she had been told.

'Oh I thought it was quite amusing,' I replied as I moved on to the tea room where Keith was waiting.

There was no doubt that the happenings in Ireland never ceased to amuse me. On another visit to the Emerald Isle Craig and I were walking through a large shopping mall when I passed a man wrapping his tongue around a large ice cream. Not being able to resist the temptation of enjoying the same we entered the shop he had come out of just as the assistant in the store had made a large softy ice cream with a chocolate flake sticking out of it, and looking around could not find the customer who had ordered it. Turning round to the nearest man she asked if he had ordered it.

'No,' he replied.

'Well would you like it?' she asked.

'No,' he said. 'I have just paid and asked for a plain ice cream,' he assured her.

'You can have this one free if you like,' she urged, hoping to get rid of the cone.

'No, I want the one I paid for,' he demanded.

'OK, would you like this ice cream free?' she asked as she turned to me.

'Yes, thank you,' I said, delighted as I walked off with a delicious cone, leaving Craig to pay for his own. After all, that is what we went into the shop for in the first place.

I was not the only one who found the Irish funny. My mother-in-law was tickled to death with their antics when we took her on a visit to see Craig's new house. She was 89 years old and although she could walk she could not manage long distances so we hired a wheelchair from the Royal Hospital in Minton to take in the boot of the car for our ferry journey to Ireland, so that we could show her in comfort the sights of Ireland during her stay. Her first close encounter with the Irish was one day while I was pushing dear Mother-in-Law around the village where Craig lived, in a mission to find John the village maintenance man. He was the one who took pride in keeping the village tidy and was paid 25 hours a year by the council to do so: he had told me this one afternoon when I was chatting to him while he was gardening when he stopped suddenly and asked me the time.

'I don't work a minute over my paid time,' he had said.

Craig had just had a large patio laid in his back garden and the wooden crates that had carried the stone had been left behind, and I thought perhaps John would be able to use them for firewood as he seemed to find a use for everything he found.

After pushing Mother-in-Law to one end of the village with no sighting of John, only the evidence of the recent work he had finished earlier that day such as the freshly cut grass at the entrance to the village, we made our way to the other end of the village only to spy him busy clearing weed from under a hedge. We approached him and took time to compliment him on his hard work before I casually asked him if he would like some firewood, rather than me get rid of it to the tip.

'Where do you live?' he asked. And in an attempt not to seem too keen he asked, 'And what kind of wood is it?'

Holding back my smile at his inquisitive look I gave him the address and said I would put the kettle on if he was calling. He replied that he would give us time to get home and then he would follow us up the road. I turned the wheelchair around to make our way back home quickly and before we had gone 50 yards he was behind us with his tractor and trailer. I took to my heels and ran, with Mother-in-Law whizzing along in the wheelchair, laughing at the experience of being chased by an overgrown elf-like man with thick white hair in good supply and a long white beard to match, sitting on his very old battered red tractor which was pulling an overloaded trailer; no doubt some discovered treasures he would recycle.

When we reached the drive of the house I breathlessly shouted to a surprised Keith to get the kettle on as the villager was coming to tea. John enjoyed a 'Leave the tea bag in the cup,' as he requested.

Rather than take the wood he sorted out the leftover stone in the pile and said he would come back later for the wood once he had emptied his trailer. Later that afternoon we had the pleasure of seeing a very happy John leave with yet another full trailer, and we in return had a clear patio area, having enjoyed an entertaining day in the process.

Before the end of Mother-in-Law's holiday we managed to fit in the Tullamore Show, a big annual event that all surrounding villagers and farmers usually attended to sell or display their crafts or cattle, whatever it might be. Since it took place 12 kilometres from Craig's home it was ideal for us to attend, complete with an adequate picnic prepared to enable us to spend some hours looking around the different events that were laid on. What we were not prepared for was the physical effort it was going to take to push a wheelchair through a churned-up field that was used for a car park to be able to reach the pathway that led to the entrance to the main events.

Give Mother-in-Law her due, she never complained about the roller-coaster ride she put up with as we pulled her backwards (finding this the easiest way) through the uneven furrows of the field car park to our destination. But she found the whole journey worthwhile once mingling with the locals, who all had a kind word for her and even offered her cups of tea while she sat watching the prize bulls being shown around the ring, led by their proud owners in the hope of winning the rosette and the money that went with it.

Yes, Ireland had its characters although it might have lost one across the water to the delight of the population of Bendigo when Kyd joined the practice in 1988, bringing a little of his inherited charm of Ireland with him.

17

Making a Change

Our group practice, Boweryhill Surgery, used to consist of six male partners with no female partner (until 1992 when two female partners, Dr Goode and Dr Breeze, joined. Because of this I felt that women in our practice were not offered any integrated positive approach to healthcare, and that there was a need for a 'Well Woman' type of clinic, run by a female, as some women are apprehensive about discussing their problems with a male doctor. Such a clinic could help to encourage more continuity of care and integrate various screening procedures that were then done in a haphazard form into an organised Well Woman Clinic.

With the approval from the doctors in the practice it was quickly agreed that the idea was a good one. As a practice nurse I was in the fortunate position of being able to spend more time with the patients than the doctor; my role as practice nurse consisted of caring for the individual and their family as a whole, and this included counselling and nursing guidance to patients. Women felt at ease discussing their problems with me.

Firstly I made arrangements to visit a local factory whose workforce comprised mainly of women (750), and by means of a questionnaire I interviewed 40 ladies during their lunch break, to find out their views on such a clinic. I wanted to know if their doctors in other areas provided a Well Woman Clinic, and if they had ever attended one: if so, was the service they received satisfactory, and did it meet their individual needs? If they had not attended one, would they attend if they were given the opportunity, and what services would they like to see offered to them?

After gathering this information I then approached a heavy engineering factory, and asked the men if they would design a poster advertising a Well Woman Clinic for me to display in the surgery, with the health of the women in their life in mind. This proved very helpful; it also gave the men food for thought and made them consider their partners more.

The next step was to find out from a section of the ladies within our practice whether there was a need for such a clinic: this was done by handing out a questionnaire to each lady that attended the surgery one morning. After speaking to the ladies, I was surprised at their eager response. I found that they felt anxious about 'wasting the doctor's time'; a lot of the women had social problems rather than physical and wanted to chat and felt more able to do so to another female. I was well aware that the proposed changes would lead to an increased workload for myself, and would involve time set aside from the already busy working week for such a clinic. Why not? The need was there.

At the next practice meeting I put forth my suggestions to implement my clinic: the only initial problem was of staffing, because during the time that I intended to hold my clinic I would not be available for nursing duties in the treatment room and this would cause some difficulties particularly if one of the other nurses was away. Nevertheless the doctors were keen, as they knew such a clinic and its inception would be of value to the surgery in a number of ways:

- It would give an opportunity for women to discuss their problems with another woman.
- It could give an opportunity to encourage women to take part in the mammography programme which had recently been instituted in our area.
- It would decrease the doctors' workload, easily measured from the point of view of cervical cytology, but probably for other consultations too.

- It could increase the uptake of cervical cytology and immunisations (with a corresponding increase in practice income).
- It would allow an opportunity to discuss with women in their forties and fifties the advantages and disadvantages of hormone replacement therapy.
- The clinic could be of great value in the detection of abnormalities such as hypertension and diabetes by routine screening.
- Finally I could give an opportunity to discuss other aspects of health education such as smoking, obesity and diet.

Increasing services such as cytology and vaccine immunisation would encourage a positive attitude to health care amongst patients, and could be remunerative to the practice.

The first decision was when to arrange to see them. I planned initially to see them on a one-to-one basis, at a time and date convenient both to the patient and myself. I was aware that some ladies wish to be seen on the spur of the moment and need to be given the chance to express their anxieties there and then. If they are not given this opportunity they might not return, building up their anxieties within them, therefore I intended to be flexible with this clinic; the time of the clinic was arranged by taking into consideration the advice given from colleagues to suit the patients, without disrupting the normal routine running of the surgery and other clinics.

Wednesday afternoon, and my appointments for the Well Woman Clinic were fully booked when a receptionist phoned through to me to ask if I could possibly squeeze in another lady who had just turned up without an appointment. After enquiring who the patient was, I realized she was someone that did not often attend the surgery and that she was due for a check-up, therefore I instructed the receptionist to fit Betty in with me at a given opportunity.

Betty, a small slightly overweight lady, had called for her routine cervical smear test, and knowing how much of an effort it had taken for her to do so I was pleased I had not turned her away. She was only 4 foot 11 in height and her short legs could not quite reach the couch. This was soon rectified when I helped her onto the examination couch by aid of a small footstool. Once Betty was undressed and lying on the couch she anxiously called to me, 'I don't want that machine,' (indicating to the speculum) 'Oh no!'

After great persuasion on my part and having given her a full explanation that the task could not be done without the use of the 'machine', I at last carried out the procedure and once I had finished pulled the screen around to allow her to dress. Having washed my hands I turned back to my desk, then I heard a thud; little Betty had fallen off the couch and rolled under the screen. This happened because she forgot to use the footstool. Surprisingly she got up unhurt, dusted herself down, and turned to me and asked, 'When will I get the results, nurse?'

Betty, who had taken falling off the couch and landing on the floor all in her stride, was puzzled by my shocked expression, and wondered why I sat with my mouth open and took so long to answer her.

Some women will agree that having a smear test can sometimes be a traumatic experience, and if so this could affect a woman's acceptance of screening in the future. However, much depends on the woman herself, and the importance of trying to be relaxed during the examination: when they are tense it becomes more uncomfortable. Such was the case with Molly, who had an appointment with me for her routine cervical smear. She came into my room very nervous about the procedure; this was not unusual as most ladies feel anxious before having their smear test even if they have had one before. Molly took her time explaining why she had come then made her way behind the screen where she slowly undressed for the task and eventually got up on the couch.

Knowing only too well how she was feeling I tried to put her at ease by chatting to her as I carried out the smear, in an effort to take her mind off what was happening. I said, 'Your hair looks nice.'

Much to my shock this comment had an adverse affect. Immediately, in a state of panic, the lady sat bolt upright and asked, 'What hair do you mean?'

'Why, the hair on your head.' I replied, surprised at her question. To which Molly, rather relieved, lay back down again. I was just grateful that, because I was at the foot end of the couch, she could not see the grin on my face as I tried to complete the task in hand without laughing aloud.

After Molly had managed to pull herself together and retain her composure before bidding me goodbye, I felt I had earned myself a cup of tea before my next appointment, and went off to make one.

With tea break over, my next patient was a young mother called Sarah, who came in to see me accompanied by her small son Justin aged three. Once in the room the little chap marched right up to my chair and standing under my nose he said, 'I do have a healthy diet.'

Being rather amused by young Justin I replied, 'I am sure you do.'

Justin frowned at me before he replied, 'But I am bored.'

Tickled to death by this little chap I smiled as I said, 'But you've only just come in.'

The amusing thing was he was just having his say after having to wait longer than he wanted to in the waiting room, so he decided to get in first, even if the appointment had been made for his mother for a Well Woman Clinic.

Implementing a Well Woman Clinic had without any doubt increased my workload immensely, but although there was very little spare time in an already busy working week one can always find time to do what one feels the need for: in my case it was this clinic. The need of the patients varied with each clinic. With some patients it was just a case of listening while the women related their anxieties or worries; with others it was practical skills needed, for example the taking of cervical smears.

While counselling some of these ladies I found there was a need for more clinics. Non-smoking would be of great benefit to them in the future. I enjoyed the sessions as most of the ladies were self-referrals and it gave me a feeling of job satisfaction to be able to answer some of these questions and where possible alleviate some of their anxieties. Each clinic was booked with no difficulty and most ladies kept their follow-up appointments.

The running of the clinic gave my colleagues the opportunity to refer ladies for certain services and so enabled their own appointment times to be used for other patients with different needs to be seen by them. The fact that the appointment book was full, and that some new patients had been referred from ladies that had previously attended a clinic, was an encouragement; some ladies telephoned to ask if they could attend because they had heard about it from a friend but they were not registered with our practice and asked if they could they come privately. Unfortunately they could not, but what they were entitled to from their own surgery was the offer of protection against the flu.

In order to enhance patient care by reducing the number of patients requesting treatment for flu during the winter, and help benefit the practice in terms of income, we organised a flu campaign to take place between 8.30 and 10.30 on one of the first Saturday mornings in October, when the flu vaccines were due to be delivered to the GP surgeries across the country, hopefully to be administered to the population before the winter flu had a chance to take hold. On the chosen Saturday the nurses in the practice would arrive at the surgery for 8.15, ready to treat the queue of patients who were already lining up outside the surgery doors all having the same thing in mind – wanting to be first.

The Flu Day campaign has proved effective over the years by the sheer number of patients who have faithfully come year after year; the attendance in the early years was around 250 and over the past few years increased to 600 seen within the two hours. The day was always a popular social event, both with the patients and the staff and because it was held on a Saturday and not a normal working day it never felt like a task. We administered the flu vaccine in a fun way, military style: the reception staff would take the patients' details before asking them to roll up their sleeves ready to receive their jabs. This is when the fun would start with clothes flying everywhere. Women would not hesitate to pull arms out of their jumpers, displaying all styles of undergarments, while the male gender would be only too pleased to tell us how it reminded them of their days in the armed forces when they were lined up to be jabbed in the line of duty. Alongside the discarded items of clothing would fly the banter from the patients that kept us entertained as we worked our way through the list of people.

The patients enjoyed the social side of the event so much that they would show their disappointment if they missed the Flu Saturday and had to attend an individual appointment in the week to have their flu vaccine. As for the nurses, by the end of the flu session we would be shattered, but certainly enjoyed giving up our Saturday morning to entertain the community that we served, knowing that there is clear evidence that the flu vaccine is safe, effective and cost-effective in reducing influenza infection, especially in the elderly and those with chronic medical illness.

The role of the doctor changed on the Flu Saturday mornings, when occasionally the doctor (usually Dr Breeze) would make the coffee and would supply us with cream cakes which we devoured at the first given opportunity – a lull in the queue of patients, usually only at the end of the session.

I always thought that we could have made the most of this Saturday if we had taken the initiative to have supplied the patients with tea or coffee to buy, but practically there was no room in the waiting area for them to linger before or after their jabs, although I am sure the patients would have appreciated such a gesture and might have been only too willing to help out and even make the tea if given the opportunity.

The idea of so many of the practice population turning up so faithfully to have a vaccine every year never ceased to amaze us as nurses: the fact that the flu jab was free and not always in endless supply might have been a factor in the number that attended: after all if something is advertised on the media as being in short supply (as the flu vaccine has often been) then human nature makes it likely to be in demand across the country causing a rush to obtain it.

After our initial flu session we would visit the elderly in the care homes in and around Bendigo where our patients on the practice list were residents. Here we would give the flu vaccine to people who wanted to have it in an attempt to protect them from what could prove to be fatal to the vulnerable.

18

Two Special Hens

After Dr Samuels retired, Dr Goode and Dr Breeze joined the practice. It was good to have female partners again and the female population in the practice were delighted to have lady doctors; this was obvious, with their surgery appointments always being fully booked.

Dr Goode was passionate about the care she gave to her patients and often she would voluntarily follow up on their progress to ensure that their health care was complete, sometimes by telephone whenever she had a spare moment between appointments. To some extent she would burn herself out workwise by using every spare moment she had to treat her patients; often if there was a given opportunity such as a gap in her surgery appointments due to a late cancellation she would carry out a home visit or two. Doing so sometimes caused her to miss her lunch break, but rather than keep a patient waiting she would go without.

One afternoon after a very busy morning she rushed out to do an emergency home visit and when she came back to start her next surgery she was absolutely soaking; it had rained all day Dr Goode had got wet going from her car to the patients' homes where she had often had to wait for a time on the doorstep while the patient struggled to open the door. As usual she had given so much of her time to the patients that she did not have time to go home for a change of clothing before her afternoon surgery was due to start.

When she sat down at her desk her wet hair dripped onto her computer keys and she was surrounded by a puddle at her feet caused from her drenched skirt. Shivering, she switched on her PC to view the list of patients who were booked in to see her.

'You can't sit there so wet, you'll be ill,' I said, concerned about her.

'I'll be OK. I must get on and see to my patients who are waiting,' she replied.

'I'll go and fetch you something of mine to wear,' I suggested.

After leaving her room I hurried down the corridor to inform my colleagues that I would not be available for a few moments, before going off home (five minutes in the car) and returning with one of my skirts. As soon as Dr Goode's next patient came out of her room I went in and insisted that she changed before seeing anyone else, if only for her own comfort. After a little persuasion she did, and completed the rest of her surgery appointments a lot drier while the staff set to and managed to dry Dr Goode's own skirt in time for her going home.

It was inevitable that when Dr Goode decided out of the blue to take early retirement, it came as a great shock to us (her staff). The thought of losing such a good doctor was not one we relished; on a personal level I regarded her as a friend and she had always been so helpful to me with any problems I had gone to her with concerning a patient, or advice on how I should deal with the treatment of an individual person that presented with a difficult diagnosis. I valued her as a thoughtful GP and I was certainly going to miss her. When the news got out, her patients were to say the least disappointed that she was leaving, and although they naturally wished her well they also knew that she would be difficult to replace.

Apart from being a very caring doctor she was also a very clever doctor when it came to her professional knowledge of medicine and this was another asset we would lose. She was known for her love of animals and was the proud owner of a few which included horses, two llamas, chickens and a dog, so it should have come as no surprise to us that when we asked her (because she was so practical) what she would like to have as a leaving present, she said that given the choice she would really like 'a special bred hen'.

Such an unusual request meant we had to ask around, making enquiries as to where we could obtain such birds. To our amazement one of the nurses, Val, had a sister who just happened to breed such hens so, when the time arrived to obtain the gift, Val went off with Flo the secretary to collect not one, but two, Special Hens. Flo (who by the way had to hold the box containing the birds while Val drove) took a liking to the hens on the journey back and volunteered to keep them overnight in her home until the following day when she would bring them in for Dr Goode's last day at work.

When Flo got home the only place she could think to put them was in the downstairs toilet of her new house. At the time it seemed like a good idea, but this did not prove to be such a good thing as was discovered in the morning when she opened the door of the toilet and found hen droppings and feathers everywhere, all over her new walls and tiles. It had not dawned on her that this might happen.

The disruption they had caused was not forgotten as Flo had still the mess to clean up when she got home, but this was put aside as the delighted Dr Goode on the afternoon of her last day joined the staff for a buffet lunch upstairs in the practice. There, instead of being presented with a fancy present tied up in ribbons, she was more than thrilled with her cardboard box containing two Special Hens which she thought she might name after two of her partners as a reminder of who she was leaving behind to carry on the good work. After enjoying a natter with her while we ate her special cake (decorated with animals) we bade our farewells before we watched her leave the surgery and make her way across the car park, trying to see through the brown feathers that were flying from the box which held the 'Specials' as she carried them to her car. Sad as we were to see her go we knew that there were at least two additional members to her household who would be glad that she would now be looking after them.

As for Flo, well she was not likely to forget the hens in a hurry, especially when she got home and she still had their mess to clear up after a day at work, so I suppose the following was inevitable. It was a busy morning in the treatment room when all of a sudden I heard a thud from behind the door that led from the treatment room into the corridor leading to upstairs, where the secretaries and clerical staff had their offices. I inquisitively opened the door only to find Flo in a heap at the bottom of the rather steep stairs. Knowing Flo as I did – she was always up to tricks, anything for a laugh – I was not too concerned because I was convinced this was just another one of her pranks, especially since she did not look too bothered or hurt. I laughingly ask her what was the matter.

'I fell down the stairs,' she said, still smiling.

'Oh yes, and how did that happen?' I asked, disbelieving.

'My heel caught. I really am in agony,' she grinned.

Still not convinced, but having a grain of doubt, I leaned forward. 'Let's get you on your feet,' I said, trying to get her up.

On one foot Flo was wearing a high, stiletto-heeled shoe while the other foot was shoeless. The other shoe which she held in her hand, had its heel snapped off. After a quick examination of Flo injured limbs, despite the fact that we both could not stop laughing we agreed that she should be checked out at the hospital and arrangements were made for another staff member to drive Flo to the Accident and Emergency Department at the Royal Hospital.

A few hours later Flo was brought back to the surgery looking like a hopping disaster; one of her wrists was in a plaster cast, the other was in a splint: she had a sprained ankle and was wearing a collar support holding up her head. My first reaction on seeing her was to think this was a wind-up, and her way of getting back at me for all the pranks I had played on her and other staff members in the past.

How wrong I was. Flo really had fractured both wrists (not

166

ideal for anyone, especially a secretary) and because physically she would not have been able to cope with both her hands out of action by putting her two wrists in casts, the Casualty doctors had spared her by just plastering the one. To accompany these injuries she had a sprained ankle and a neck injury. This turned out to be yet another unexpected day at the surgery. I am happy to say that eventually, after a period of sick leave, Flo returned to the practice and was able to carry out her professional duties, perhaps initially a little slower to start with, but before too long she was back to her old self.

Flo was not the only member of staff to suffer from a fractured wrist. When Dr Breeze joined the practice it proved to be a great advantage having a young lively lady doctor: she was full of energy, and not having enough dashing around the practice during a typical busy day, she decided to take up skiing lessons with her family (husband and three children) before going off to ski in Austria. This become a regular occurrence, even though after one of her earlier visits on the ski slopes Dr Breeze returned to work with her wrist in a plaster cast.

Despite the fact that she was severely incapacitated she could not let her patients down by staying away from the practice and instead struggled on seeing her patients and attending to their needs one-handed. This was no easy task: apart from the obvious practical procedures being difficult for her at times it was not easy using her computer one-handed.

Her patients loved her: she like her name was like a breath of fresh air, everyone found her easy to talk to, and talking came as no problem to her – some say she could talk for England. That was the only problem Dr Breeze talked so much to her patients that it caused her to run late for her appointments, although the other patients booked for her were quite prepared to wait to see her however long that might be, because they appreciated that once they actually got into her room they would be given the same amount of time. She had a gift of knowing just how to put her patients at ease, by complimenting them on their appearance or asking them where they had got their lovely shoes from. Most things came naturally to her and, it would be fair to say that they felt she was their friend rather than their doctor, and sometimes said so.

Working with Dr Breeze was great. She enjoyed life and knew how to have fun; she was always the first to join in if her staff were up to any pranks in an attempt to liven up a dull day, and it was the same when it came to going out socially with her – we would appreciate her great company and knew it would not be a quiet night out. On the night of Heather's wedding Dr Breeze danced with the rest of us.

I had my part to play when Heather, the cleaner from work, got married. Keith was not the only step-in chauffeur in the family: a few weeks before her wedding Helen asked Dr Mo if he would be her chauffeur and drive her in his white Mercedes to her wedding. He was only too pleased to be asked, and agreed to do so. Unfortunately the day before the wedding Dr Mo discovered he was down for the emergency on call duty the next day; he tried in vain to exchange duties with some of his partners but alas no one was free to do so.

As a last resort he asked me if I would step in to save the day and drive Heather in his car to the church. Reluctantly I said I would if no one else was available. I secretly hoped I could pass the duty on to Keith, but unfortunately he was unable to stand in because he was working, so I was left with the honour of taking Heather to get married and the responsibility of the white Mercedes, Dr Mo's pride and joy.

The big day arrived and Keith gave me a lift to Dr Mo's home to collect the car. Dr Mo had invited me take the car the night before but I did not want the responsibility of the car left out all night while it was in my care, so it was no hardship to go for it on the morning of the wedding. As I drove this lovely vehicle home I felt as if I should have been giving everyone the Royal Wave, but instead I kept both hands on the steering wheel, and watched my speed like a hawk and applied my Highway Code, which was spot on. Once I had the car on my drive I set my sights on preparing to decorate it fit for a bride, by putting the white ribbons on and silk roses in the back window. As I stood there in my smart trouser suit I knew there was something missing, then it dawned on me it was not the car that lacked the final touch, it was me, so off I drove to put it right. I drove to Jackend where I parked outside the undertakers and went in and asked the surprised undertaker if I could borrow a chauffeur's cap to complete my look. Perhaps it was just having the cheek to ask (the undertakers hire out for weddings) but I came out of the undertakers adorned with my cap.

I arrived at Heather's home which was a hive of activity with the last-minute titivating being applied to the bridesmaids, and other members of the family all dressed in their finery. At last the bride and Rob (her dad) were ready, so we set off on our journey, and what a journey it turned out to be, Rob looking as if he had just stepped out of Hepworth's window. One could have been led to believe that this was the case, because sitting in the back with her dad Helen discovered his suit still had the price tags hanging from it and the pockets were still stitched up: apart from this, the price stickers were still on the soles of his new shoes. So it was that the lovely bride spent her journey to her wedding trying to remove all the evidence that showed the cost of her dad's new attire before he gave her away to her groom.

The wedding went off well, helped by the laughter we shared on the journey, thus paving the way for what turned out to be a fun day and an even livelier evening. However, having completed my duty I returned Dr Mo's car safely to him before I attended the events of the evening reception, even though he did say I could have kept it for the weekend – a temptation I had to reject.

19

This Is Your Life

After 30 years at the surgery Dr Blessington had seen some changes, including with the building itself, with walls being knocked down, built up again, and broom cupboards made into consulting rooms, and the pram area made into staff rooms. This was done in an attempt to house the extra staff employed to enable the practice to move forward and meet the needs of the growing number of patients joining the list, plus the extra demands required complying with the ever-changing paperwork for the health authority.

There were changes also in the staff, who came and went. Like the trainee doctor that applied for a job: he actually lived in his car, and when he arrived for his interview the staff slipped out into the car park to have a look in his car while he was being interviewed. There was everything you could imagine crammed into every nook and cranny, including the kitchen sink in his car. He did not get the post as this was not the image the practice wanted to portray.

Another young doctor applied for the post of trainee and everything appeared suitable, the interview was going well and he looked like a promising candidate; that is, until just before the interview ended, when he mentioned that he could not drive. Unfortunately for him, driving was an essential requirement to be able to carry out home visits, which at that time was a large part of the daily duties carried out after morning surgery (how things change). Once he was made aware of the requirements he said his farewells and went off to book some driving lessons.

Then there was the trainee doctor who got the post, Dr Ford, who was a keen biker. While he was employed at the practice he lived in the flat above the surgery, so it came as no surprise when he was found mending his motorbike in the flat – the oil stains on the stairs were a real giveaway. Dr Ford was such a lively, fun-loving chap, a delight to have in the surgery. When he was not biking he was rock climbing, another of his energetic hobbies, and it was during one weekend while he was climbing in Wales that sadly this young man was killed in an accident when he fell from a great height. The doctors and everyone at the practice who knew him, albeit only for a short time, were devastated at his sudden death, ending what was a promising career.

We could not allow Dr Blessington's retirement to go without a bang, so a few months before his retirement, unknown to him, both the staff and partners in the practice put their heads to-gether to plan a good farewell for a man who had served his staff and community well. Each evening when he left the practice after finishing his surgery, the staff would discuss the special night, and those that had been in hiding (not supposed to be on duty) would come out of hiding and we would start to rehearse our song and dance routines, where I planned to incorporate his 'This Is Your Life' story in the form of a cabaret.

Having decided to do 'This Is Your Life' for Dr Blessington's party, my mission was to try to get someone famous to present him with the Big Red Book. I started by contacting various TV celebrities by letter, asking if they would come and acknowl-edge a man that had served his community not only by ad-ministering his medical skills, but also as an active member of the Minton Lions. He had given so much to the charity or-ganisation, giving up his free time, and not afraid to dress up in all kinds of outfits collecting funds in all weathers. However, all my efforts came to no avail, although I did get the odd reply stating I might get some obscure personality if we were willing to pay a massive fee.

Giving up this idea as a lost cause, I contacted Dr Munro in

Scotland and asked him if he would do the honours to his first trainee doctor. Dr Munro was delighted to be asked and arranged to travel back to Shropshire with his wife, Dr Turnball, for the special night. With Paulette's help I collected their family photos and family history along with names of friends and relatives who should be invited. Armed with the facts, over several evenings Paulette and I put together the story of Dr Blessington's life, he himself being completely unaware of our secret meetings held at my home in order to do so.

Dr Goode and I trailed around at every given opportunity after surgery in search of the right caterers for the night, and Dr Mo was put in charge of recording the event on film, using his latest video recorder. The Gaye Theatre at Daisywood provided us with some of the costumes; other costumes were either made, or borrowed from whatever source available.

The big day arrived and it started off with panic, not to mention agony, as Heather (one of the cleaners) arrived somewhat slowly at the emergency Saturday surgery suffering with a very painful haemorrhoid. However the duty doctor, who happened to be Kyd, came to the rescue by lancing it with a very sharp scalpel blade: after all, the show had to go on that night and Heather had a big part to play.

The venue for the party was at Buildwas Abbey in Buildwas. This made a lovely setting, with part of the Abbey church and cloister (which are in the guardianship of English Heritage) in the background. I am a member of the Abbey Crown Green Bowling in the private grounds of Buildwas Abbey which made it convenient for me to arrange the events of the night.

Dr Blessington was on a fortnight's holiday and on the given night Paulette had told him they were invited to a friend's engagement party. Because he was on holiday well away from the surgery and out of earshot of anyone letting the cat out of the bag, he did not suspect anything. At seven o'clock on the dot the practice staff all arrived at the Abbey, laden with last-minute goodies to put in place on the tables and in plenty of time to greet the guests who were due to arrive by 7.30 and had travelled from as far away as France, Scotland and other parts of the globe, to honour such a gentleman.

The room, which was the banquet hall in the upper floor of the Abbey, had been decorated to perfection, which included a life-sized painting of Dr Blessington borrowed from his home and placed on the wall above a special chair. After keeping a watchful eye out for the doctor's arrival I gave the warning to the guests that he was about to make his entrance. There was a hush in the room as everyone listened to him climb the stone steps of the winding staircase and waited for the large wooden oak door to open, as it did when the special guest entered the room, followed by his wife. Dr Munro stepped forward and, handing Dr Blessington the Big Red Book and announced, 'This Is Your Life, Dr Blessington.'

It was a good thing there was a large armchair waiting for him, because the surprise made his legs weak as he sank into his chair and tried to take in the sea of faces that surrounded him.

Once the applause created by the guests had quietened down, Dr Munro started to tell Dr Blessington's life story and, as rehearsed, between each aspect of Dr Blessington's life Dr Munro would pause for members of the staff to enter the room and perform a song and dance routine to music, acting out each stage of interest corresponding with the tale being told. For example the cancan dancers appeared, tying in with his life in Paris, while the gaps in between the cabaret were filled by various friends and family members whom he had not seen for years making their entrance, to the surprise and delight of the good doctor.

As for Heather, she danced as well as the rest of us, despite her minor operation in the morning.

For the grand finale, all the members of the practice who had taken part in the show gathered at the feet of Dr Blessington and sang:

We'd like to keep you here with us
But know you have to go
We've made this effort as you see
To put on this fine show

We'll miss you buzzing on the phone
And ringing that damn bell
Now Tracy thinks she's gone to heaven
But really she's still in hell

Chorus:
You're a real gent
That's what we'd like to say
Few and far between
As we've found out today
. . . You're a real gent

We've shared some laughter through the years
And some have shed some tears
You've helped us through our trying times
And helped to calm our fears

No more haemorrhoids warts and nits
And no more 'spots' and zits?
And no more notes to go astray
That sure will make your day

Chorus:
Room 1 will be the big white chief
Room 2 will be so mad
Room 3 he wants a quiet life
Room 5 he is so bad

Room 6 is in a dizzy spin
Room 7 feels so blue
Just look at who you've left us with
We think we'll retire too

Chorus:
Room 4 will never be the same
What are we going to do?
There's no one that can take your place
Because we're losing you.

This resulted in our star guest having to wipe away a tear that managed to escape from his sparkling eyes; we who witnessed it were not quite sure if it had been caused by the emotion of the evening or if it was the fact that he had to endure such dreadful singing – after all, he was himself a talented musician. The evening was a great success, thanks to the tremendous effort everyone had made in trying to put on a Palladium performance to entertain the guests who had come so far, and to give a fitting tribute to a good man.

A tribute everyone was thankful they had attended, because very sadly Dr Blessington died after only a short period into retirement at the age of 67 – a devastating loss to his family and friends. The grief was repeated a year later when Dr Samuels died after a short illness at the age of 73, yet another sad loss to the people who knew and loved him.

20

Friends We Meet Along the Way

The thought of having every Monday off for a year appealed, but the thought of all the studying and mental fatigue was not at all appealing. However, I was pleased to have been given the opportunity by the Shropshire Health Authority to do the Health Education Certificate course at Radbrook College in Shrewsbury, and the extra bonus had to be that the health authority would fund the cost of the course. It was the idea that it was not going to cost the practice anything that had swayed the GPs into allowing me to be away from the surgery on a Monday (one of the busiest days in the week) to attend the course.

When I arrived at Radbrook College on the first Monday I was surprised to find that the rest of my classmates attending the course were from different disciplines in the health service such as cardiac nurses, dieticians, health and hygiene, and district nurses. I was the only practice nurse on the course and this made me appreciate the chance I might have to gain knowledge and insight into the work my fellow students did. The variety of health care workers proved to make the course interesting and once we were all made fully aware of what each other's jobs were and what they entailed, it became invaluable in my everyday work in the future, especially when the occasion involved having to refer patients to others who were more appropriate to deal with the individual's problem.

With such a mixed group of individuals Monday was not without its aspects of fun. I am reminded of the time when we were receiving a rather serious lecture from a visiting speaker, the group were giving the lecturer their full attention and apart from the teacher's voice you could have heard a pin drop. At least, that was, until Paul (a male nurse from the cardiac unit) dug me in the ribs and whispered in my ear, 'Where have you left the other part of your gorilla outfit?'

It was winter, and I was wearing a black long-haired mohair hand-knitted jacket and the cool air had made the mohair static so it fluffed up every fibre, leaving my garment standing on end and me looking like I had just left the zoo. I cannot remember the end of that lecture as Paul and I both spent the rest of the lesson trying to stifle our giggles. Fortunately for us the main tutor who ran the course and, more importantly, marked our exam papers, was not present that morning to witness our behaviour.

Throughout the course we would be given topics to present and talk about to the class. One student chose to talk on bereavement. Not an easy subject, so she started off her session by trying to get her fellow students to relax. To do this she asked us all to lie on the floor, close our eyes and listen to some of Handel's *Water Music*, it was just after our lunch break and within minutes the whole class had fallen asleep. By the time the student woke us all up her allocated time to present her talk was almost over: needless to say, I certainly, and I am sure the others, looked at bereavement in a totally different way from then on. As to what marks she might have received from our tutor I am not sure, because the tutor herself might have enjoyed a quiet nap.

One week we were asked to give a presentation to the class on what our individual job was. I presented my role as a practice nurse as likened to that of a circus act, and displayed the various tasks along with the surgery staff members as many of the acts that might be performed at a circus, highlighting the ups and downs that could occur each day. This the class found not only amusing but appropriate, as they knew me to be a bit of a clown in some way or another.

The year seemed to pass quickly with the completion of the course ending with a team building effort where we had to travel to Wales and spend a weekend living together to try our skills on a variety of assault tasks (normally the type of thing carried out by the Army) in the form of such things as rock climbing, canoeing, map reading, rope climbing and abseiling. On the whole we had to learn how to survive, and perhaps the most trying was the living and sleeping together in what only could be described as very basic facilities with no frills attached. Our sleeping accommodation comprised of bunk beds where the person on the top bunk had to make sure they did not fall out, and the person on the bottom bunk had to watch they did not bang their head too often on the bed above. However, the communal showers had to be the icing on the cake with cold water to make sure we were wide awake and to stimulate or shock us into the action planned for us that day. This topped it all.

My greatest achievement that weekend was to complete the challenge of abseiling; as one who has always been afraid of heights, I never thought I would have made it along the narrow ledge that led up to the point of the cliff from where we were expected to abseil down. Once I had started up the path I had no other choice but to continue upwards, because the group of team mates following behind me left no room for me to pass them to descend when I tried. And believe me I did try, when at one point I suddenly froze and thought I would go back down. Eventually, after what seemed like an age we reached the top where I panicked and shaking from head to toe I told the guide that I could not step off the cliff. The guide, seeming to take no notice (he no doubt had seen it all before), but reassuring me, put the harness and rope on me before I could ask, 'Does my bum look big in this?'

He asked me to trust him and turned me around to face him and holding my hands firmly, he then instructed me to edge my heels off the cliff before taking my first step down. I can only say it was a total act of trust that led me to let go of that man's hands, and gripping the rope that was hanging from my harness I started to descend the cliff face. After a few steps down I plucked

up courage to look below and seeing some of my fellow classmates at the bottom I waved to them before completing the descent.
The lower I got the braver I felt, until I was able to carry out a
conversation with the students below. The feeling of satisfaction
as my feet reached solid ground was fantastic. Whether or not I
could do it again I am not sure.

Each one of us took something away from doing the Health
Education course. I myself gained an understanding that one
does not wear white trousers while canoeing, because when white
trousers get wet they become transparent, which I found out to
my cost when my bed mates decided to tell me after I had spent
the best part of the day oblivious to the fact that everyone could
see my pants through my thin wet trousers. When the weekend
drew to an end we each said our goodbyes, knowing more about
our fellow students than perhaps we wanted to know, before
joining our various friends and family who had travelled to Wales
to take us home. Keith arrived, accompanied by Huw and Velma,
two of our friends, to pick me up. He was shocked and hardly
recognised me as I stood before him in my bedraggled state,
looking worn out, and shattered due to the physical activities
along with the strain of trying to keep to the tight schedules demanded. This, combined with the lack of sleep caused by not
enough hours in bed painted its own picture. Keith looked even
more bewildered as I excitedly related what a great time I had
endured; after all I had met some new friends along the way.

Some people bring out the best in you, and this was certainly the case with Gail. I first met Gail when she and her husband
Derek moved to Shropshire when Derek became pastor of the
Baptist Church which I attended. At that time I had just been
approached and given the opportunity to read a new degree introduced for practice nurses at Wolverhampton University, which
would be funded by Shropshire Health Authority finances which
included reimbursement to the practice to pay for a replacement
nurse in my absence, presuming I was accepted on the course.

The GPs eventually were persuaded that should I get through

the two-year day release course it could prove to be beneficial to both the practice and patients alike: the downside was that I had to find a replacement nurse to help with the workload and cause as little disruption as possible with the everyday working of the practice on the days I would be absent.

One Sunday morning while I was in church my mind wandered onto who I could get to cover for me at work so that I could apply to start the course. The obvious solution was to pray about it, and if I was meant to apply the Lord would provide someone. When I opened my eyes they fell on Gail sitting on the front pew. I knew she had been a midwife before coming to live in Shropshire and therefore had a good knowledge and experience of nursing, so I decided to ask her after the morning service if she would be interested in the post.

Once the service was over it was the custom to invite those in the congregation who wanted to have tea or coffee to gather in the school room at the back of the church where a member would provide them with refreshments and usually homemade cake or biscuits. So it was that while we were having coffee, I asked Gail if she would like to do some practice nursing. Even though it was a discipline of nursing she had not done before, she was keen to accept the challenge. The fact that it would be part-time would help her cope with her busy home life as well. I left the church that morning amazed at how quickly a prayer could be answered; now I had to convince the GPs that Gail (who they did not know) would be the ideal person to care for our patients over the period of time required.

Trusting my judgement, the GPs employed Gail for two days a week, one of which would be my course day providing I got through the university interview. The day of the interview arrived and as I descended from the train at Wolverhampton making my way up to the university I could not help but wonder whether this was what I really wanted. A few minutes later, as I sat alongside a number of younger applicants waiting to be seen, I worried that I might be too old.

After a time we were taken into a room and asked to sit around a boardroom table where one of the course tutors addressed us and laid down criteria that had to be met before commencing the study. After hearing what was required academically, some candidates left because they did not meet the given guidelines; others left because they felt, having received the information, that the course was not for them. I sat a little bewildered until I was personally approached by the tutor when I heard myself say, 'I think I have the required criteria.'

The tutor then completed the introduction to the course by taking each remaining person aside and carried out individual interviews. While she was talking to me she sifted through my CV at the same time, before asking me to fill out an application form at the reception desk on the way out. It was a lovely sunny afternoon and I was soon making my way back to the train station and remember thinking as I walked on to the platform, 'What will be will be.'

The two years that followed proved to be hard work, studying and trying to get assignments in on time while doing a full-time job was not easy. There just did not seem to be enough hours in the day to fit it all in. I would be just getting into the flow of an essay that had taken me all evening to get into, when Keith would pop his head around the door of my study, telling me it was almost midnight and time I switched off the computer and got some rest

'Yes I will just finish this article and be up in a minute,' I would reply.

Then, after what seemed like no time at all, I would glance at the clock and, seeing it was 3 a.m., decide I had better get to bed before the alarm was due to go off four hours later for me to get up for work. Quietly slipping into bed without disturbing Keith was an art in itself but one I managed to perfect over the months.

During the last semester of the course it was brought by some of the other students to the tutor's attention that I was only allowed to have the day I was attending university away from work, and that I should, like the others on the course, be having at least another day off work to study and time to complete my research. Most of the other students were full-time at university, and those who were like me doing a day at college were only working part-time at their practices, which gave them time in the day to catch up with their studies.

The fact that the health authority were paying for me to do the degree and also funding the practice to provide cover meant that they intervened on my behalf and informed the GPs that I had to be allowed the study time. The extra day away from work relieved a lot of the pressure for me and gave me time in the day to contact those I needed to in connection with my research, which claimed a great deal of time and effort. It also allowed extra paid hours for Gail, which helped her financially as well as giving her more time in practice to be able to gain experience that she might be grateful for in the future.

Working alongside Gail was a joy in itself; she enjoyed the work and the patients loved her – the way she greeted them made them feel it was her pleasure to attend to them, and her pleasant approachable manner made it easy for the patients to relate to her and discuss their problems. Gail had a special rapport with the children; having her own grandchildren made it easy to understand their little ways, while teaching them came as second nature to her, especially as she taught in Sunday School several weeks of the year.

Gail had not been at the practice long before it was her fiftieth birthday, and as it was the custom with the staff to do something special to mark an exceptional occasion, we pondered over what we could do to surprise her. Eventually I came up with an idea and, knowing how Gail loved the children, I approached the local primary school and asked if they would allow a group of children to be brought to the surgery in order to sing 'Happy Birthday' to her on the afternoon of her birthday. After a great deal of persuasion (because of the many child protection and safety rules to abide by now in place), and a few consultations with the school teachers, they at last agreed with me that it would be a nice gesture (as a majority of the children knew Gail), if two of the teachers would bring a choir of children to the surgery after lunch.

Unknown to Gail, who was busy in the treatment room, the children filed into the waiting room taking their places beside the patients who were booked for the afternoon appointments and preparing to perform their sing-song. At the given time Gail was asked to go into the waiting room on a false mission. As she entered the room the children stood up and sang, much to her and the patients' surprise. Gail could not have shown more delight if she had been handed a diamond ring. However, once the children had finished and left the surgery, she did say, 'How amazing it was that all those children should come at the same time to be treated!'

The staff all laughed as they explained to her that it was by special request, and as we helped her at the end of the day carry her various birthday gifts (given by the staff) to her car she said, 'What a lovely birthday I have had.'

Two years of brain-storming, long hours of studying and constantly thinking of the next work assignment and deadlines to meet the course, were at an end. Along the way I had met some great students who I had bonded with, knowing they too were struggling along the same route as me, although perhaps I might have been struggling more than some. I had enjoyed finding new avenues of knowledge and at last I had managed to complete my research. My help had come from above: it was all an answer to prayer without which I would have given in and returned to the easy path of going back to the work I knew and was familiar with – especially as some obstacles had appeared during the two years.

Gordon, my brother-in-law, died (Nancy's husband) and the emotional pull to give my time to family was strong. Mabel, a nursing colleague who I worked alongside for 19 years, died and

I did stop to think, should I be carrying on with my studies at such a time?

But yes, it was all meant to be, and the day of my graduation confirmed it to me, with the thrill of knowing that most of the set of students had achieved their goal adding to the excitement of that day as I stood being fitted with my cap and gown accompanied by Keith and our son Craig. The two of them were bursting with pride, especially Craig, more so Craig who having himself been adorned with cap and gown not once but twice in the past, was delighted to guide me through the protocol of the day, before taking me to lunch prior to the ceremony. When my name was called out and I walked across the stage to receive my scroll I could hardly believe that it was really happening to me, the lass from Lanark, now a Specialist Practitioner in Practice Nursing BSc Honours. Yes indeed, it had all been a wonderful answer to prayer.

21

Coping with Loss

The shock of the sudden death of colleague and partner Dr Gardener back in 1991 stayed with the practice for some time. In fact it took a few years for the staff and patients to get over the loss of a good doctor. He was only 48 years old when he left the surgery fit and well (to everyone's belief) to go on holiday with his family, and died while away, which all made it difficult to accept as any signs of health problems had not been apparent. The gap he left in the practice proved impossible to fill.

He was much loved and missed by his patients and this was apparent at the first antenatal clinic following his death, when his patients who attended were seen by another doctor. Most of them were reduced to tears as they found themselves overcome with emotion as some inevitable changes to their care were explained to them.

Dr Gardener was the third young staff member I had seen the practice lose since starting there: the first had been Dr Ford's fatal accident during his weekend in Wales. The fact that he was only in his mid to late twenties at the time of his death had a profound affect on the practice staff, many of whom were the same age as him. Only a few years earlier Pauline, our practice manager, had died in her early forties after a short illness, sadly leaving a young son. The Christmas before Pauline died she was very ill in the Cottage Hospital in Minton. A few of us (in an attempt to brighten her day and at the same time try to include her in our events) dressed as Christmas boxes piled into a car, left the practice and set off to see her. The only problem was that the boxes were not designed to sit down in so as we sat in the car they lifted just enough to almost strangle us. The journey from Bendigo to Minton was almost suicidal but well worth the agony just to see the delight on her face; fond memories.

Throughout the years that followed there were other colleagues who sadly passed away, some who also had worked alongside Pauline, one of which was Sally, a receptionist who had been a fun loving person. In the past she had helped to support the local community to raise funds, when needed for the church hall. Many a time she would offer to help with the costume making. Or get roped into taking part in the occasional Christmas pantomime held there. Sadly Sally died after a short illness. I remember that when Sally was ill at home I had just recently bought my new scooter, and was keen to show it to her, so one winter evening after work I set out in the dark to Sally's home. Up until then I had only used the scooter for work during the hours of daylight and that was just as a means to get back and forth from Bendigo to the garrison Army camp, a distance of about 4 miles, to help with the clinic there. So Keith was reluctant to let me go out on it at night, thinking I might kill myself or someone else, but because of the circumstances in this instance I was able to convince him I would be OK. Which I was, at least going to Sally's home, but coming back home was another matter.

After a short visit that lasted about an hour I said my goodnights to Sally and John, her husband, and left feeling quite confident about my riding skills. However this bubble was soon burst when not far into my short journey my front wheel hit a pot hole in the road and I went head-over-heels in the dark, landing on my right side with the bike on top of me. I was not hurt, just stunned for only a second or two before I jumped to my feet to pick up my new bike to examine the damage. Fortunately, from what I could make out in the dim light, there were just a few scratches on the red paintwork where the bike had scraped along the road surface. I was relieved to see that there were no dents or broken mirrors: landing on me had cushioned the machine, which I was not sorry about.

However, since I was nearer my sister Margaret's home than mine I thought it might be a good idea to compose myself before I got home, and hastily made my way to her, pushing my bike. Within moments of ringing her doorbell, the door was opened by a surprised Margaret.

'What have you done?' she asked.

'I have just come off my bike, but I'm OK.'

'Look at the state of your anorak.'

In the light of the room I could see that the right shoulder of my jacket was ripped and all down the right side there were several patches of tar blobbed here and there.

'Never mind, at least it's not the bike,' I sighed.

A cup of coffee later, and after I had tidied myself up, I set off for the second time that evening to go home. Keith shook his head when I told him what had happened and was just pleased to see me home in one piece; he had never wanted me to have a scooter in the first place, and felt I would be much safer with four wheels under me than two. He was right.

That evening was the last time I saw Sally: she died not long after.

Then there was my nursing colleague, Mabel. She had completed her nursing training at the Shrewsbury Infirmary, and after getting married had moved from her home town of Shrewsbury and bought a house in the Rosebank area. She found the commuting to and fro from home to work not only expensive, but the extra time allowed for the journey was making it a long working day for her.

So when the previous practice nurse, Isabel, was leaving to have her baby, Mabel joined the team at the surgery as a new practice nurse and we worked together until she went into hospital to have an operation. This was when it was diagnosed that she had a terminal illness. Up until then Mabel had been employed at the surgery for 19 years and was good at her job: she was another young person to die in her early forties.

Then there was Dr Mo, who bravely struggled into the practice to carry out care for his patients when he himself was not at all well. Here he would treat and sympathise with people who were in better health than he, until he just did not have energy to cope any longer and had to give in to his illness. He was latterly admitted into the hospice in Shrewsbury where he sadly died on 26th January 2001 in the early hours of the morning, and because of his religion he was buried some hours later on the same day.

Due to the suddenness of the funeral his family were aware that their Western friends and patients did not get the opportunity to pay their respects, so in an attempt to rectify it Dr Mo's wife and family asked me if I would arrange a memorial service on 29th January 2001, some three days later, in an attempt to address this. Given that there was such a tight time limit I thought that the quickest and most far-reaching method of advertising this was to contact the *Shropshire Star* (the local newspaper) reporter to publish an article on the life of Dr Mo and his service to the community over the years, at the same time alerting those who might wish to attend the Pinza Suite at Bendigo Town Hall where the venue was to be held. Little did I know until the day before the service that the reporter I spoke to earlier in the week had gone off sick, and the report had not reached the news desk. Then after making some frantic phone calls to the same newspaper, I was given profuse apologies from another journalist and a promise that an article would be published that day and would appear in the evening paper.

The following day I could only hope that most of the practice population had seen the article which had been printed as promised the previous evening, and that some at least would be able to attend the service. The surgery was closed from 1 p.m. until 3 p.m. with emergency cover only in the afternoon until the service was over, then once again the routine appointments would commence. The memorial service, which took the form of a tribute to the life of Dr Mo, was very informal and very pleasant, with different family members and friends sharing their own fond members of this much-loved man. Many of his patients too, even those in wheelchairs, had managed to get there to present their own amusing tales, causing quite a lot of humour as story after story was related. A nice tribute to a man who had in the past shared a good sense of humour with those he came in contact with. This was a comfort to both family and friends alike, finishing the afternoon with a cup of tea and biscuits before we headed back once again to unlock the surgery doors, fully aware that a large part of the heart of the practice was no longer there.

These were popular members of staff who were liked by those who worked with them and came in contact with them, and because they all died at a young age this made the loss difficult to cope with.

It is always sad when we lose someone we know, and especially when it is a child. Deep sorrow was the feeling I had when Tom, a four-year-old patient, died shortly after the practice had moved to Bendigo. I had not been at the surgery long when I met Tom, who had cystic fibrosis; this is one of the most common genetic diseases, and it is estimated that almost 20 per cent of people carry the gene, which must be present in both parents to cause the disease although Ireland has the highest rate of cystic fibrosis in the world, where 1 in 19 Irish people are carriers of the gene.

However, Tom was English and due to his illness he was a regular visitor to the doctor who, after seeing the boy, often referred him to me in the treatment room to give the little chap an injection. This is when Tom, whom I remember looked like a little gent in his tiny overcoat, would stand and swear at me like a trooper after I had given him the nasty needle.

The grief his family endured at his death was unimaginable. I could only relate to how I and the staff at the practice felt when this little boy was no longer on our list, and how I knew no other child would make me smile as he did when he rebuked me.

Some days just don't turn out like you would expect, and this particular Friday was one. The morning had been busy, but no busier than usual, for the last surgery appointments before the weekend. Then just 20 minutes before lunch time the most un-expected thing happened. Cathy arrived at the reception desk ac-companied by a lady who asked the receptionist if Cathy could see a doctor.

Cathy was a chronic asthmatic patient who we all knew well, and she usually needed urgent treatment if she turned up without a booked appointment. This was one of those occasions. The re-ceptionist took one look at Cathy (who was in a state of near col-lapse, gasping for breath and barely able to speak) before running to fetch medical aid, which turned out to be myself and another nurse who the receptionist met in the corridor.

Hurrying to Cathy's aid we did not hesitate in getting her into the nearest consulting room, where within seconds she collapsed just as two of the GPs who the receptionist had found still in their consulting rooms came rushing in to help in the treatment.

The next 30 minutes or so were spent administering emer-gency treatment to Cathy while we waited for the ambulance to arrive. It was the most stressful half-hour, trying to resuscitate a dear lady who I had known and nursed for many years, and had watched her family grow into adults who also were registered at the practice. After what seemed like an age the ambulance arrived and took Cathy off to hospital.

When we returned back from lunch we were saddened to hear that Cathy had died in the ambulance. What seemed to have made matters worse was that the friend who had brought Cathy to the surgery told the staff that she wanted to take Cathy straight to the hospital, which she had to pass on her way to the surgery. But Cathy had insisted that her friend drive her to her own doctor, who Cathy had every faith in – wasting time had been a big factor in this tragedy.

Over the years Cathy had been encouraged by the medical staff to try and improve her lifestyle by giving up smoking, a habit that she failed to master and that ultimately worsened her asthma, causing side-effects that had led to her death.

So the week ended on a sad note, leaving me with a weekend of reflection. Could I have done any more for this dear lady, who had such a likeable personality? Knowing her and the family for many years made her death feel more personal to me. The reality of how quickly a life ends, and the finality of it, brings home the urgency of being prepared to met our maker. I knew as I applied pressure to Cathy's chest in an attempt to revive her that my silent prayers for the Lord to intervene did not go unheard, but that it was His time to take Cathy from this earth.

The sobering reality of an unexpected death did not always occur within the surgery walls. One crown green bowling evening when the Abbey's male team had an away game at Jackend Club I went with Keith to watch him play. It had been raining off and on all afternoon and although it had stopped by the time the match started at 7 p.m., the grass was wet.

'Lynn, would you please mark Keith's score cards while you're here?' asked his captain.

'Yes, no problem.'

This was usually the case. Apart from making me feel useful, it meant I had to concentrate on the game, which had not long got under way before the unexpected happened. One of the Jackend players, who was on the opposite side of the green to where I was standing, walked down towards the jack having just bowled his second wood, when he appeared to have slipped on the wet grass, landing on his back with a thud. I instinctively dashed to his aid, only to find the sportsman had collapsed suffering a massive heart attack. I performed emergency resuscitation on him while his brother (who also was a bowler) knelt beside me desperate to help. The emergency services were contacted immediately but because of the location of the bowling green, which was at the end of a long path, behind a high hedge, and hidden from view of the main road, the ambulance had difficulty in finding us.

By the time they did get there, the bowler's wife had been

191

fetched from her home, still wearing her slippers, now soaking from the wet grass. As I laboured over this poor man, surrounded by his friends and family members, I failed to see any response and was very glad to see the ambulance crew hurry onto the green to take over. Although I knew he was already dead. His wife, who later sent me a thank-you card, was comforted by the fact that her husband had died in the company of his friends and playing the sport he loved. Ironically his opponent Neil experienced the same thing two weeks later when another bowler he was playing against from a different team collapsed on the green and died on his way to hospital, leaving some team members a little wary of playing against Neil for a time, not to mention how shocked and uneasy Neil felt about the experiences he had been unfortunate to be involved with.

This experience led me to identify the need to update professional training in administering emergency resuscitation within the surgery, and a few weeks after that sad night 16 members of the primary healthcare team received training.

22

Nothing as Funny as Folks

It was a Thursday afternoon and I was carrying out heath checks on diabetic patients prior to them being seen by the doctor in his diabetic clinic. These checks included taking the patient's blood pressure, their height, weight, checking their urine, measuring the patient's waist measurement, blood tests, examining the condition of their feet, and various other checks including the patient's eye sight.

It was while I was carrying out Alice's diabetic check that I asked her, 'How is your eyesight?'

Alice, a pleasant, elderly lady, with a good outlook on life, replied, 'I have no problem with my eyes.'

'Well, why are you wearing odd shoes?' I asked as I looked at her feet. She was wearing a black flat-heeled shoe and a brown high-heeled shoe.

'Am I?'

'Yes. One shoe which is a different colour has a heel higher than the other.'

Unperturbed, Alice looked at me shrugged her shoulders before saying, 'I thought I had a limp.'

Finishing the appointment with Alice, who had been the last for the diabetic clinic that Thursday afternoon, I glanced on my computer screen to see the last name on my list, who was a 'heart-sink' patient, and known by all for his moaning. He would moan about the weather, he would moan about how long he had to wait at his last hospital appointment, he would moan about the consultant he had seen there, he would moan because he was expected to moan. Having been forewarned that he was next in, as shown on my PC screen, (he had come in for a routine dressing on his sore toe), I was ready to greet him with a big smile followed by a funny comment that took him off his stride and his usual opening moan.

He even forgot himself at times and laughed a little as I fussed around his poor painful toe, and then it happened: I was trimming the surrounding hard skin on his foot when the blade slipped and cut his other toe. Alas, because the patient was on medication that thinned the blood, he bled more than normal because the clotting factor took longer, and this proved difficult to stop. His blood was everywhere and as I struggled to clean him up as quickly as I could I fully expected him to create a fuss. Instead he surprised me when he said, 'Don't worry nurse, I bleed for hours.'

He had forgotten all about moaning and seemed amused at what had happened or perhaps at the shocked expression I was wearing. Whatever it was, he took his leave from me in a somewhat chirpy mood. In fact, he looked rather pleased at having two dressings applied instead of the usual one: perhaps it was the thought of the tale he could relate once he got home about the nurse's appointment and her carelessness. Nevertheless he continued to book appointments for my surgery and appeared happy to see me.

Monday morning, and it was my 10.55 appointment, the last one before morning coffee break, when I called Sylvia, a chronic asthmatic lady who I knew well, to come in to my room. As she entered the room she stated, 'Nurse, I do feel ill – I really feel ill.'

Knowing her past medical history I enquired, 'Well, it's not your asthma is it?'

Sylvia looked at me, surprised, before she replied, 'No – but I do feel ill.'

After I had asked her about the symptoms and the onset of the problem she explained, 'Well you see when I got into bed last night my husband put the hot water bottle in the bed, and it burst on my muffty. Well, the pain was terrible.'

I tried in vain to conceal my laughter as I replied, 'I'll tell you why you feel so ill, you're in shock. It's what you might call a hot flush.'

This resulted in us both laughing so much I had to help her back out to the waiting room, where everyone in the waiting room thought she was in distress. Instead, she could not stand up for laughing.

'Oh! I do feel well,' she was heard to say. 'I never saw the funny side before.'

It goes to prove that laughter is the best medicine. I did not have to administer any treatment for Sylvia, her own laughter did the healing.

My first appointment after lunch one Friday was an Irish patient called Mrs O'Ross. We had shared some stories in the past about the similarities between the Irish and the Scottish and she had informed me that the only difference between the Celts was that the Irish could swim. The appointments Mrs O'Ross had kept in the past were to seek help for the problems she had with her lower region of her anatomy. This resulted in the GP referring her to see a consultant to help rectify the unwanted haemorrhoids, perhaps by removing them.

On this particular Friday afternoon Mrs O'Ross had called to tell me the outcome of her appointment with the consultant; she related to me the conversation that went on between her and the consultant.

As she entered his room the consultant greeted her:

Consultant: 'How are you?'

Mrs O'Ross: 'Well, Doctor, I have had this trouble down below for some time.'

Consultant: 'Have you been to the toilet?'

Mrs O'Ross: 'Yes doctor.'

Consultant: 'Long ways as well as short ways?'

Mrs O'Ross: 'Both, Doctor.'

Consultant: 'Well you do dress nicely,' as he admired her outfit.

Mrs O'Ross: 'I do my best.'

Consultant: 'I am sure you don't want me to fumble down there, do you?'

Mrs O'Ross: 'That is up to you, doctor.'

Consultant: 'No, away you go, and see how you are. See your own GP if you have any more trouble.'

Mrs O'Ross came out of his room very despondent. After she had informed me of the outcome of her hospital visit she arose from her chair, and as she opened the door to leave turned and said, 'I waited three months for that appointment.'

Before I called for my next patient I could not help but wonder if the fact that Mrs O'Ross was Irish, with a great sense of humour which she never failed to show, had stopped the consultant from taking her seriously by not picking up on how much discomfort and pain she was suffering with her haemorrhoids. Or had he mistaken her for being Scottish and, like the reputation that goes before a true Scot, he might have thought she could not bear to part with them. I never did find out, because as far as I know Mrs O'Ross is still hanging on to her haemorrhoids to this day.

Mrs O'Ross was not the only patient to want to hold on to her 'bits', troublesome or not. Charlie was another who arrived and asked me if I could relieve him of the unwanted ear wax causing him to be dull of hearing. After checking that his ears did need syringing, I took him to the treatment room to wash out his ears.

Now most nurses will admit that syringing ears, although the outcome is usually satisfying for the patient, is not the nicest procedure to carry out. The sight of sticky, dirty wax coming out of someone's canal, especially when it is more commonly a man's hairy ear canal where the wax clings to the hair follicles on its way out and the nurse has to end up picking it off in order to clear the canal.

In Charlie's case his unwanted plug of wax swam out in one

big lump, hitting the kidney dish with a bang, much to Charlie's relief and surprise. Because he was so delighted that he could hear it fall he asked, 'Can I take it home with me?'

'I don't think so,' I replied in disgust. As I quickly flushed the offensive lump of wax down the drain. The thought of some unfortunate relatives having to put up with having to examine Charlie's wax was too much. Them having to endure him boasting about the size and details of the wax as they sat around the dinner table would be bad enough; the act of me actually picking it up and presenting it to him to take home was not going to happen.

The tale of wax went on as a young man came into see me later that day and complained that he was dull of hearing and asked if I would check out his left ear for him. After an examination of his ears I explained that only his left ear was blocked with wax and would require syringing.

Taking him into the treatment room I asked him to sit on the swivel chair while I carried out the procedure. Once again I checked his ears, and turned to collect my equipment. Before I proceeded to carry out the task I turned the young man round in his chair and syringed his ear. On completion I waited for him to leave the room, which he hesitated to do.

After a few minutes in which the young man remained rooted to his seat, he turned and asked, 'Will that help the blocked ear?'

I had only syringed the wrong ear.

The young man's appointment was followed by a rather agitated patient (Ted) who arrived for his appointment and on entering the room stated, 'Why are these ears blocked? The frustration of not hearing properly, is causing me to lose my temper more at home, and the family have sent me to have something done about it.'

After I examined his ears I told him, 'It's wax. I will syringe them.'

'What, now?' he asked. 'I thought I had to soften the wax first?'

'Yes, normally you would have to come back after using oil to soften the wax, but let me try to remove the wax first since you are so troubled with it.'

After I had carried out the procedure of syringing his blocked ears, I proceeded to lead Ted to the door and bid him farewell.

However, he was reluctant to leave and asked, 'What about my blood test?'

'What blood test?' I asked.

Ted went on to say, 'I had a form for a blood test for Nurse Smart.'

'Yes, that's me.'

As I checked his medical records there was no evidence, no clue to be found about a request for any blood test.

'What was it in connection with?' I asked.

'I have a numb thigh.'

I searched the records again. 'You were seen by a doctor eight months ago,' I stated.

'Yes, I lost the form and have just remembered,' he vacantly replied.

So in a final attempt to cheer Ted up I took a sample of his blood in an effort to solve the problem of the once numb thigh which he had first experienced all those months ago.

The last appointment of the day brought in Alan to see me: yes, you've got it, complaining that his ears were blocked and re-questing that I syringe them. After I had completed the exami-nation and confirmed that his ears needed syringing, I carried out the task, which successfully cleared his blocked ears.

When Alan saw the contents that came out of his ears he said in amazement, 'What is that? Old age?'

'No!' I said, 'They call it earwax.'

Some tasks that have to be carried out are not always pleas-ant: in fact some are quite mucky, but where there is muck there's money. This was certainly the case with big Jim, a larger-than-life local character who occasionally came into see me: only oc-casionally, because he was too busy making money to waste time visiting the surgery, let alone going to the trouble of making an appointment to see a doctor where he would have to waste time sprucing himself up to do so. No, instead he would call in, mostly on spec, to see me. At such times he would arrive just as he was, straight from work, having made no effort to tidy his appearance beforehand.

I liked Jim, he appealed to my sense of humour, and I felt I could say anything to him and he likewise would say anything to me. I knew that whatever advice I gave him regarding the welfare of his health he would take on board, and try his best to comply with any treatment given. His appearance made me smile and added to his colourful character; he was usually unshaven, un-washed looking and wore a jumper with more than one hole in it. On his feet would be a large pair of heavy-duty steel-toed boots, the type that would need a good pair of strong ankles to be able to lift them just to walk. To me Jim was like a big gentle giant, but I was informed that this was not always the case; apparently there was another side to him.

I was told of one instance when he was in the cab of his lorry driving down a narrow road, when another vehicle coming in the opposite direction would not give way or reverse to allow Jim to pass. Jim being Jim was not going backwards, especially when he was in a hurry to go forwards: the fact that the other driver was a neighbour of his seemed to make the matter worse, so after several heated words exchanged between the two drivers they both decided to squeeze past each other. As the two drivers came level with each other Jim without hesitation put his large fist through his open cab window and reached through the open window of the car and punched the offender on the nose.

I thankfully never experienced any of Jim's short temper; instead I always found his visits to me for treatment entertaining. After he had told me how everyone – or so he thought – was out to rob him of his hard-earned money and usually it was (according to him) his own family, he would go on to tell me some story or another while I treated him for whatever he had the matter at that time. On one visit he told me about the time he went to buy a new lorry: he had gone to a dealer in Wolverhampton and as always he had gone in the middle of his working day. After he had walked around the outside yard inspecting the lorries for sale, he walked into the show room and had a look before he entered the posh polished offices, where he was met by a young man wearing a smart suit who turned his nose up at Jim and his grubby appearance before rudely asking him what he wanted.

'I've come to buy a lorry,' grunted Jim.

'Oh yes,' mocked the young salesman as he tried to lead Jim out through the door.

'Well, do you want my money or not?' said Jim. Jim then reached into his dungaree pocket and pulled out a huge wad of notes. 'I'll pay cash,' he continued, as he threw the money on the salesman's desk.

The young man gasped as he looked at the thousands of pounds in front of him, then turned on his heel and brought Jim a leather chair to sit on, quickly followed by a cup of tea handed to him in a china cup and saucer. Jim sat down, put his big feet with his dirty boots on the fancy coffee table, and drank his tea.

'You see he didn't think I had the money.' He winked at me as he left the treatment room.

23

Seeing the Man

How wrong can one be about people and how often do we judge people by their appearance? Donald was a gentleman who over the years had attended the surgery with one problem or another, and at first glance could be taken as being somewhat eccentric in his appearance. He would arrive at times still wearing his slippers, and his clothes would still be carrying the remains of the previous night's supper: his thick black hair would have been combed back held in place with thick Brylcreem. But when Donald opened his mouth to speak there was no doubt that he was an educated man from a good family background where he had not wanted for anything. He now lived alone in a small bungalow in Bendigo with a home help who attended to him once or twice a week.

Because of Donald's appearance, he had unfortunately been taken advantage of by some members of the community at various times. During one visit to me he told me that just before he left the house a young man had called at his home and asked him for a drink of water. Donald, being a kind man, had asked the young man to wait at the front door while he fetched the water. Once the young man had drunk the water and left, Donald discovered the money that had been in his coat pocket had gone with the unwanted visitor; the coat had been hanging on a hook in the hall behind the front door. The surprising thing about Donald was that as he told me the story he held no malice against the man; in fact there was even a touch of pity in his voice as he spoke.

Each time Donald attended an appointment with me to receive treatment to have his leg ulcer dressed he would related a poem or a saying or a funny tale that he remembered from his youth. Here is one of the last poems he recited to me:

> Sometimes when you're feeling important
> Sometimes when your ego's in bloom
> Sometimes when you feel that you are the
> Most qualified man in the room
>
> Sometimes when you feel that you're going
> Would leave an unfillable hole
> Then think of these two little verses and see
> How they humble your soul
>
> Take a bucket and fill it with water
> Put your hands in it up to the wrist
> And then pull them out and the hole that
> Remains is just how much you would be missed
>
> You can splash up the water and churn it
> And you can make ripples galore but
> Take your hands out in a minute it
> Will go just the same as before
>
> The moral of this tale is quite simple
> Always do the best that you can
> And remember that there is
> No indispensable man.

This was told by one who would appear to be quite an in-significant man, not much to look at, but once he had been given the opportunity he proved to be a fountain of knowledge. Proving the saying, never judge a book by its cover – or does it?

One of the attractions of working in general practice is that no day is repetitive: this is because of the people we deal with and the unpredictable things that we come across each day. One such afternoon started with the arrival of a new patient.

I came out of the treatment room to call my next patient waiting to see me, when to my surprise sitting in the front row of the waiting room was a new patient who was certainly different in appearance to any other patient I had ever seen in the surgery before. The rest of the regular patients waiting to be seen had moved away from him to the back of the room, and anyone coming in took one look at our new patient, then joined the others by squeezing into the back of the room. Sniggers could be heard behind hands and mutters behind the reception desk. As I looked at this new patient my first reaction was that of pity, so I asked this man to come into the treatment room, away from staring eyes.

This tall, well-built man with broad shoulders was wearing a dress and coat, with high-heeled shoes on his large feet, and he was carrying a duck-handled umbrella. It was the duck umbrella that seemed to add to the mockery, and a further problem he had was that he was still growing whiskers, which was not out of place with his large 'Adam's apple' and very deep voice, but did not look right with the bright blue eye shadow dabbed on each eyelid, below his thick, bushy eyebrows.

'I have come to see a doctor,' he said.

'Yes, but I thought you might feel more comfortable waiting in here,' I suggested.

'Well, I am not sure if the doctor will accept me on the list.'

'Would you like me to find out for you?'

'Yes, please. I have been turned down by other practices in the area.'

With his consent I went off and asked the doctors if they would be willing to accept this man on our list. Their answer was as I expected.

'No problem, but put him in to see one of the other doctors, as I am about to go out on a home visit,' said the doctor.

Leaving the doctor's room I headed up the corridor to ask another doctor if he would be willing to see this 'new patient', given his unusual appearance.

'Of course. He is a patient, after all,' said the second doctor I had asked.

It did not matter which doctor saw him, he needed to be seen by someone: after all this young, mixed-up man was in my opinion in desperate need. I went back to the treatment room to reassure the patient.

'There will be no problem with you registering at the surgery,' I told him.

Feeling more at ease he then started to open up while he waited to be called, and told me how he had moved from Birmingham to the Rosebank area because of the problems he had experienced in the office where he worked.

'But what does your mother think?' I had to ask.

'My mother and my family could not accept me at first. People are laughing at me.'

'But can you wonder at it?'

After all it was Bendigo he was now in, and he certainly was not the everyday person you would expect to pass in the street, especially when it wasn't Halloween.

After that first appointment he visited the surgery once more, then we never saw him again. Whether or not he went back to Birmingham to live I don't know, but I do know that this was a poor soul who needed help, perhaps more mentally and spiritually than the intervention of surgery that he was seeking to alter his voice box.

He was not the only person who passed through the practice on a flying visit. Throughout the year the practice takes on temporary residents (people living in the area for a short time). Some of the most interesting temporary residents who turned up at the surgery annually were our gipsy travellers, and although colourful characters they were on the whole very grateful for all the care they received.

One afternoon a traveller and her four-year-old daughter arrived at the reception desk asking if her child could be seen. The receptionist, after checking the appointment book, rang through to the treatment room and asked me if she could send the little girl in to be treated; the little girl had a nasty cut on her leg. It was quite unusual for them to attend the nurse because the travellers I had dealt within the past were normally reluctant to seek outside help and would administer their own remedies if possible.

The child who was brought in was very pretty, with long blonde hair, and tanned skin due to her outdoor lifestyle. She was well nourished and quite tall, which made her look older than four, and despite the fact that she had a large laceration on her right leg caused by her falling on some glass, she was not crying. After I had checked her over I explained to her mother that I would have to put stitches in her daughter's leg in order to get it to heal properly. Mum accepted that it had to be done, and the child made no fuss throughout the procedure of first cleaning the wound before injecting a local anaesthetic in her leg, then stitching this tanned little limb.

The little girl sat and watched me without even flickering an eyelid when she saw the needle being pushed into her leg. As far as I was concerned, I had never experienced anything like it in an adult never, mind a child. The little girl's skin was as tough as leather which meant I had to apply some pressure to enable me to get the needle through the tissue: the thickness of her skin caused the first suture needle to snap. Even this did not make this child flinch: she was a perfect patient. After completing the stitching with a new needle the little girl smiled at me before trotting off with her mother, back to the desk to make a follow-up appointment in a week's time for her daughter to come back and have her stitches out. What surprised me the most was that the little girl's leather-like skin had cut so badly in the first instance. I would have thought it was too tough for glass to have damaged it since it managed to break a stainless steel suture needle.

Some of these travelling ladies are surprising. I remember when

I was a midwife one antenatal lady being brought into the labour ward in Shrewsbury Hospital. This traveller was in her thirteenth pregnancy and within an hour she gave birth to her baby girl who weighed in at 12 pounds. It was the largest new baby the maternity unit had seen born there at that time: the healthy infant looked like a three-month old baby, and when she lay in her cot in the nursery she looked as if she had just eaten one of the tiny tots that lay in the neighbouring cot.

The excess weight of this baby was amazing when I considered that my own mother only weighed 2 pounds and 2 ounces when she was born, no heavier than a bag of sugar. She was so small that my granny's wedding ring fitted on Mother's wrist like a bangle, and in an attempt to keep her warm my granny put her to sleep in a pie dish padded with cotton wool. It obviously had the same effect as today's incubators since she survived to have six children of her own.

The travellers on the whole appreciated all the medical care given to them, as was the case when one of our doctors was asked to go on a home visit to see a gipsy in his caravan. This was rare, because usually they did not welcome any intrusion into their privacy and would always try and get into the surgery if necessary. Once the doctor had completed his treatment on the old gipsy man he closed his briefcase and was about to leave the caravan, when the old chap put out his hand and, shaking the doctor's hand, said, 'Thank you, sir. What do I owe you?'

With that he opened a large chest which was placed under the window of the caravan to reveal its contents – it was crammed full of money.

'Oh! No, there is no charge,' said the doctor, and he left the site and made his way back to the surgery still somewhat startled at the amount of wealth he had just seen.

Then there was the opposite side of the coin, where we were able to offer help to the patients who had very few comforts in life, like Mavis. It was another busy day in the treatment room when Mavis arrived for a dressing to be applied to her injured hand. I knew Mavis and her sister Martha, who lived with her: they had been patients at the practice for years and were real characters. One day while Mavis and her sister were passing my sister's house, Bill my brother-in-law was cutting his hedge and stopped to have a chat to them. The next thing Margaret heard was Bill calling her to bring two cups of her homemade soup to the front door, which he promptly handed over to the sisters to heat them up on such a cold day; that's the type of effect they had on some people.

Having carried out the task of cleaning and dressing Mavis's cut hand I stood back and took a long look at my patient who stood before me. She was soaking wet: it had been raining all day and I think she had walked into Bendigo from Black Wood, her hair, which was long, was dripping all down her face and neck and her thin jacket was wet through. As I glanced down at her feet I saw that Mavis was wearing a pair of canvas shoes that squelched as she walked.

'Have you no more shoes, Mavis?' Without waiting for her to answer I stated the obvious: 'Your feet are soaking.'

Mavis did not answer but looked surprised that I should be bothered about her appearance: after all, it was how she always looked.

'Just wait a minute,' I said.

I picked up the phone and rang the Salvation Army who were based across the road from the practice; ask anybody in the street what the Salvation Army means to them and they'll probably come up with a range of answers: brass bands, soup kitchens and selling the *War Cry* in pubs, but the Salvation Army is the only community-based church in Bendigo, although it receives no financial support from government funding, nor any grants, and has no community care contract with the local health authority or social services.

They have developed to meet the demands placed on them with between 600 and 700 members of the local community attending weekly. With the many services they provided, I was sure they could help Mavis, so within minutes I was encouraging Mavis to go to the Salvation Army where they would seek to find her a pair of shoes.

To my delight, two days later Mavis arrived for her follow-up appointment proudly wearing a smart pair of leather shoes.

'I see you got your shoes then, Mavis,' I stated as I applied the dressing to her hand.

'Oh yes!' smiled Mavis. 'How is it looking for a coat?'

I could relate with Mavis in an odd way: there had been a time when I had no shoes to wear to school. I was about 12 and was in my second year at Lanark Grammar Higher Grade when my black lace-up shoes (which were part of the school uniform) had worn out, and as usual money at home was in short supply. It was a case of having to make do until such time as there would be some extra available to get some shoes.

But the cloud did have a silver lining, when to my delight Jean saved the day by lending me a pair of her shoes, which were smart little court shoes with a 1½ inch heel. I felt like the bee's knees going to school that morning in the trendy footwear. However, Jean's foot was a size 4 while my foot was a size 4½. I had managed to get them on OK and they did not seem too tight at first but as the day wore on my feet became so numb and painful that I knew if I took the shoes off while I sat at my desk during a lesson, I would never stand the pain of trying to get them back on again. So I endured the agony to my crushed-up toes and swollen feet by keeping the trendy shoes on while I was at school. As soon as the final bell rang I was out of there to head straight home, even if it was a slow progress because the effort of hurrying sent shooting pains from my feet up my legs. Once home I could not get the shoes off quickly enough, but the relief was not instant: I had to wait until the throbbing had ceased in the balloon-like feet with blood-red toes. Suddenly the shoes did not look so trendy, but more like instruments of torture.

Here for the first time I knew what the Chinese women (back in history) must have gone through when they had to have their feet bound: but what I did not know then was how helpful the Salvation Army might have been.

I did know, however, that back in Lanark when my sister Margaret was a teenager, it was not the Salvation Army that had helped her gain a new pair of shoes, it was the Mission Hall. One day when Margaret was passing a shoe shop in Lanark High Street, she stopped to admire the latest fashion in shoes.

Displayed in the centre of the window, were two pairs of shoes that took her fancy; one was a pair of brogues but the other, which she preferred, was a pair of trendy court shoes. Really taken with these court shoes, she made up her mind that she would save up to buy them. A few weeks later, she was at a Sunday service in the Mission Hall and as the collection plate was handed around; Margaret, who by now had managed to save 30 shillings towards her desired court shoes, had a sudden touch of conscience.

She felt perhaps she should be putting her 30 shillings into the collection plate for a needy cause, so in an attempt to help clear her conscience, she dropped a ten shilling note on top of the plate as it passed her way, However, she still felt uneasy about holding onto the one pound note in her pocket although by now, the collection plate had been placed at the front of the altar. Margaret made up her mind, that if she was given the opportunity again that morning, she would put her one pound note into the offering.

A few minutes later, the Pastor who was coming from the back of the hall and walking past Margaret, stopped and asked her if she would kindly go to the pianist (whose piano was at the side of the altar) to ask her to play a certain hymn. Margaret, grasping the opportunity to clear her conscience, made her way to the front and, as she passed the collection plate (thinking she was not seen), she dropped into it her one pound note, and took out the ten shilling note on the top of the plate.

Strangely, she did not feel any better about her action, but did feel a lot worse when, after the service, the Pastor expressed to her how disappointed he was in her. He had seen the ten shilling note on the top of the collection plate earlier, as it was quite lot of money, and not an amount that most folk in the town could afford to give. The Pastor had not seen her put in the one pound note instead, and shamed her by rebuking her for her action.

Margaret, on the other hand, did not defend herself by explaining her exchange. Instead she kept silent, just feeling sad that the Pastor, who knew her well, and who she looked up to as a Godly man, should think so badly of her.

Just as she was about to leave the Mission Hall that morning, a member of the congregation, came up to her and said, 'Margaret, I hope I don't offend you, but would you like these?' handing her a box, 'I bought them and they are too tight.'

Margaret opened the box to find the same pair of brogues she had admired and, as she walked up the road home, she could not help thinking that, perhaps if she had put her full savings of 30 shillings in the plate that morning, she might have been carrying the court shoes home instead.

24

Tipsy in Charge of a Cabbage

One afternoon the receptionist came into the treatment room to tell me there was a lady at the desk asking for help for a man who had collapsed under the railway bridge in Bendigo. Val (one of the other practice nurses) and I left what we were doing, grabbed the surgery's battered wheelchair with its flat tyres (because it was not used much), and ran out to help. We had acquired the wheelchair from Brigend House next door one day when we were transporting an elderly patient, and they had told us to keep it. Now we knew why – they were glad to get rid of it.

After we did our traffic policeman act to stop the Bendigo traffic, we struggled to push our wheelchair across the road, and approached the small crowd of people who had gathered around a man who we could see was lying on the pavement. Once we had reassured the people in the group that we would attend to him they dispersed, leaving Val and I room to kneel beside the man, who was hanging on to a very large cabbage he had bought for his dinner.

We eventually, after a struggle, got him to his feet, which was easier than trying to push him in the wonky wheelchair. When we got the man walking we discovered from him where he lived, so delivered him cabbage and all to his front door where we left him to sober up – he had got very drunk at lunchtime in the pub just opposite the practice, and on leaving the pub had managed to stagger a few yards underneath the railway bridge before collapsing.

As Val and I walked back to the surgery to finish the job we had abandoned I remembered my days in Glasgow, when one Saturday evening while I was on night duty in theatre at the Victoria Infirmary I was nursing Harry, a very ill patient who had undergone extensive surgery. Harry was so ill that he had to be kept in the recovery room where he was monitored overnight before being moved back into the surgical ward.

Because Harry was seriously ill, his family were allowed into the theatre area of the hospital to visit him at any time. Just after 10 p.m. Sam (Harry's son) arrived to see his dad; unfortunately Sam had come straight to the hospital direct from the pub and was the worst for drink.

Although Harry was so critical he was conscious and still aware of what was happening around him, so when he saw his son it was a very emotional scene as Harry told his son how he knew he was dying, and asked Sam to pray for him. Sadly Sam was so drunk that he said he was in such a state that he could not pray for his dad, and decided he had better leave. The emotional feelings in the room that night were high, and both Sam and I were in tears as we walked from Harry's sick bed into the corridor.

My first reaction that evening had been that of anger at Sam, as I reminded him that this was probably the last thing his dad would ask him to do for him, and Sam could not carry out his dad's wishes because of his love for the bottle.

We parted company both unable to control the tears; Harry died a few hours later, but not before he and I prayed, which hopefully comforted him and gave him peace before he met his Maker. Later when I thought of Sam I wondered if perhaps he had taken to the drink to give him the courage to be able to cope with his dad's illness, and maybe he did not touch the bottle after that night.

A few years ago when Keith and I were on holiday in Scotland we were in Glasgow and I wanted to pay a visit to the Victoria Infirmary. As I stood outside the familiar building I decided I could not resist going inside to see how it had changed over the years. Once I was inside I found myself knocking on what use to be the matron's door when I worked there. The door opened and I introduced myself as one of the old staff from back in 1966, and wondered if there might be any of the old staff from that era still working there. The nursing sister I spoke to was very polite and showed an interest by phoning for one of the nursing sisters that I knew from the 1960s who was still nursing in the Vic. My old colleague came to the office to meet me and I was pleased to chat to her about the past. In return she was delighted to inform me how much the hospital had moved forward in the latest medical research; she also reminded me that Glasgow had won The 'City of Culture' award, and I responded by saying that I had been impressed by the clean-up of the stone buildings in and around the city.

'Oh, by the way,' she said, 'Glasgow only has the odd murder now.'

When I worked in Glasgow I had never thought of it as a dangerous city, and I can't say I was ever afraid to walk the streets in an evening on my way back to the nurses' home after a night out. But I do remember an incident one afternoon when I had been visiting my friend Nettie who lived on the Great Western Road (what was known as the posh end of Glasgow).

I had asked Nettie if there was anything she wanted me to fetch from the shops for her, and given an errand I had decided to go down the quiet back lane from her flat to the shops as it was quicker than taking the busy main road approach. I had just got as far as halfway down the lane when a man came from the bottom of the lane towards me. Feeling a little uneasy about him I started to quicken my step into a trot, and as I got near him I burst into a gallop to pass. Just as I did so he said something, so once I was safely past I turned and asked him what he had said.

'Would you like me to punch your nose?' he called back.

I never bothered to reply, but never stopped running until I had reached the shops. Once there I was too out of breath to say what I wanted to purchase.

Nettie was horrified when she heard what had happened, because she was such a kind Christian lady who would give anyone her last if they needed it: not that she had very much to give materially, but she always had a good word to encourage those who came in contact with her. She lived with her husband Monty her son Martin and her cat Smokey, whom she loved. Her affection for Smokey was shown on occasions when Nettie would have to scrape together enough money to buy one portion of chicken for Smokey's tea, while Monty would have the Spam when he came home from work and often because her pantry was bare. Nettie, unknown to Monty, would go without herself – that was Nettie.

Glasgow was a much better place for having Nettie; it was not unusual to see her walk along the streets of the great city handing out gospel tracts and giving those who took time to stop and listen to her the word of hope as she lovingly told them about her Lord and Saviour Jesus Christ. At every opportunity given she would invite the people of Glasgow along to the Tent Hall a interdenominational Gospel building situated in the centre of the city, where on a Saturday night it would hold as many as 2,000 people eager to hear the word of God delivered by visiting speakers, some of whom were well known in and around Scotland, some of whom were missionaries and some of whom were famous.

The weekend Gladys Aylward (the missionary whose life story has been told in book and film form, titled *Inn of the Sixth Happiness*) came to the Tent Hall, the number of people attending was in excess of the 2,000 filling the main hall to its limit, while all the annex rooms were full to overflowing with people eager to hear the great life story of such a tiny lady, of how she led the children over the mountains and out of China. As I made my way back to the nurses' home on the other side of the Clyde from the hall, I felt humbled and privileged to have heard such a lady that night in Glasgow.

Although Bill was not from Glasgow he did come from the

outskirts, and now lived in Rosebank and was registered at the practice. He was a patient I had known for many years and on most of his visits to see me I had managed to get a smile from this man who appeared to some as a serious-minded person who did not always wear a smile with ease, a dour Scot some would say, although that all changed on the day he made an appointment to see me to have his stitches removed after his varicose vein operation.

I called Bill in for his consultation at the start of my afternoon surgery and as he entered my room his 6 foot 3 inch frame limped in, legs apart as he struggled to put one leg in front of the other. Bill at the same time was too proud to show any sign of weakness, so tried to hide any sign of pain or discomfort in his facial expressions as he made a great effort to bend his knees so that he could sit on the chair I was offering him alongside me at my desk.

After a few minutes of discussing his recent operation it was time to get Bill to remove his trousers and climb onto the examination couch to have the dreaded stitches removed. This tough Scot with his long legs, which were still lined and looking like a road map (because of the skin marking from the surgeon's pen), was shaking with the thought of so many stitches, having to be removed by the stitch blade I held in my hand; stitches by the way, that were scattered all over his legs just like dead flies. The whole thing made me smile.

'Now don't you start with your jokes,' he warned me.

'You will be OK, the scars have healed well,' I reassured him.

The 'dead flies' were removed without discomfort but the next stage was not so easy. After having varicose veins removed it is a routine procedure to apply support to the legs in an attempt to prevent phlebitis and clots which could occur after such an operation; the support in this case comes in the form of white elastic stockings held up by an elastic suspender-type belt fixed together with Velcro.

Bill had to lie there on the couch while I used all my strength

215

to get these tight elastic stockings over his size 12 feet and then pull them up his chunky legs, which were still tender. The room was warm, but not as warm as the perspiration that was running down my back as I summed up all the strength I had to get these supports on him without causing him any pain. At last the leggings were on, and as I helped Bill off the couch I started to shake with laughter at the sight of this tall chap with his premature white hair, standing in front of me, legs bowed, looking like an over grown ballet-master. When I told him he was now ready to go on stage as a dancer in Swan Lake he too shook with laughter as he balanced on one leg trying to pull his trousers on.

'I shall never look at you in the same light again,' I laughed.

'Considering I was dreading this appointment I never thought I would have laughed so much,' he said, as now fully dressed he left the room. On his way out the reception staff had a rare view of the dour Scot still grinning as he walked (but not on his toes as a ballet-master) through the waiting room; a waiting room (that unknown to us all) was just about to be emptied, as I soon found out during my encounter with Mark, my next patient.

Mark had just entered my room to have his weekly routine injection, and as always Mark was keen to help. Before I had got up from my computer to pull the screen around he had dropped his trousers, wriggled down his underpants and displayed his lily-white bottom for the injection site. This action was not unusual for Mark, but on this occasion at that precise moment the surgery fire alarm went off, and although it startled both of us I decided quickly to carry out the injection. As I stuck the needle into his buttock the door of my room burst open and there stood an anxious receptionist.

'Haven't you heard the alarm?'

Her mouth fell open as she caught full view of the needle in Mark's white buttock. She quickly disappeared not to be seen again for several hours.

I looked at Mark. 'I guess we'll just have to burn,' I said, as the two of us collapsed in laughter.

'She won't do that again, come in without knocking,' Mark replied unperturbed.

Needless to say, at least three of us would not forget the surgery's first fire drill.

At a later date I was conducting another appointment with Mark, in a small, narrow makeshift treatment room that had just had new shelves fitted, and just as I reached for a syringe the new shelf collapsed, hitting me across the nose and causing me to see stars for a few seconds, leaving me wondering what had hit me.

'Are you alright?' asked Mark.

'Yes, it was just unexpected,' I whimpered.

'It's a good job you've got a big nose, Nurse,' he continued, rather concerned.

Then, matter-of-fact, he revealed his bottom to receive his injection before hurrying off to catch his bus, leaving me with a large swollen nose and hurt pride.

Now the state of my nose (it turns up at the end) could have been caused by the drop I had on it when I was a baby. I was told by Margaret who was carrying me that I was about nine months old when I wriggled out of her arms and landed on my nose. Mother scooped me up and ran down the street to the doctor's surgery, calling over her shoulder to Margaret as she left the house, 'I'll deal with you when I get back.'

So perhaps it's not surprising that my nose is a different shape to the other noses in our family. The whole incident reminds me of an article reported in *The Daily Express* dated 31st May 1943 (not that I was around then) which read:

THE UGLY NURSES
The Destroyer *Lauderdale* sent a boarding party (including the ship's doctor surgeon Lieutenant W.B. Whiston, of Edinburgh) to the Italian Hospital Ship *Virgilio* to make sure that the wounded and all else were genuine.
The Italian Commander complained to them about the lack of beauty among his 20 nurses.

Perhaps Mark had read this same article. Whether he did or not, the mishap had obviously bothered him because I did receive a letter from Mark at a later date which read as follows:

Dear Sister Lynn,

Here's hoping you have had a pleasant holiday break this last week, and one which will have presented you with total relaxation with your family at home.
I was so sorry to witness your accident with the collapsed shelf bracket recently which must have caused you a bruise for a couple of days or so. Certainly a very nasty and unpredictable thing to happen in those surroundings. Well I hope that every bit of pain and bruising will have cleared away from you as fast as possible, and that your holiday at home has been able to enhance every glad tiding focused around you.

With kind regards from your friend,
Mark.

I could only be grateful that he had not been around when my nose had sustained yet another accident while on the last day of our holiday in Ireland, when my son's Irish cat (Missy) made a dive for it as I bent down to play with her. The sight of my nose must have been too great a temptation to resist, so Missy struck out and punched it, leaving a prominent scratch right on the tip. The bleeding caused by her claw would not cease, so in an attempt to stop it I temporarily stuck a sticking plaster across my wound, and carried on with my daily chores and forgot all about it.

But I was soon reminded when I took Keith (who was out in the garden) a cup of coffee. After squinting through the sunshine at me for a second he asked, 'What have you got on the end of your nose?'
'Oh that? The cat has just scratched me.'

'Oh no, I will have to sit next to it tomorrow on the plane.'

'How do you think I feel?'

'We'll have to have separate seats.'

'I have an appointment with the opticians when I get home and there is nothing wrong with his eyes.'

'Just put plenty of powder on it,' he said, picking up his coffee.

The next day when we had checked in at Dublin Airport we were looking around the duty free shop (plaster-free) and an attractive shop assistant came up to me and asked if she could help me, as she focused in on my nose.

'You won't have enough time to help a face like that,' Keith joked.

'Did you hear what he said?' I asked.

'Yes, that's terrible. And you're still with him?' she laughed.

We left the shop and made our way through the departure lounge to board the plane. Once there I led the way up the steps to be greeted at the top by a male member of the cabin crew, whose smile broadened even more as he stared at the scratch before directing me to my seat. Then he turned to Keith behind me.

'Follow that lady sir,' he said, clearly thinking, 'Follow that nose'.

'Yes, I have been following her for years' said Keith.

When we arrived home after our travels, before friends and family enquired about our holiday they asked me, 'What have you done to your nose?'

'Oh! I've just been poking it where I shouldn't have.'

On another occasion when Keith and I were going to visit Craig, we were waiting at the departure area of Birmingham airport, when I nudged Keith to look at the person walking towards us.

'I bet she's going to Dublin,' I grinned.

'But it's only a 40-minute flight,' he said.

'She must have heard that Ryan Air can sometimes run late,' I laughed.

The amusing person now seated at the table near us was waiting while her husband went to the counter to order two coffees; he was probably glad to escape the stares the onlookers were giving his wife.

The 5' 2" woman was wearing a blown-up 'comfy' neck cushion, and if that was not enough to get everyone's attention, the colour of it did; it was shocking pink with white stripes. Her husband arrived at their table carrying the two cups of coffee, and even then the hot brew did not tempt the little lady to remove her fat pink collar, which was tipping her chin forward making it difficult to allow her to drink easily. However, she did manage to sip her drink, restricted or not.

We then made our way to the plane, leaving the pink-collared lady behind. Once we had entered the plane, we settled into the front row of the aircraft. Within seconds of doing so, a cheerful man sat beside me. The cheerful man soon informed me that he was on his way to Dublin to visit his daughter and, having arrived at Birmingham airport three hours too early for the flight, he had to spend the waiting time in the bar. Sitting beside him I was certainly sharing the fumes from the alcohol he had consumed earlier. Although the beer, he assured me, was too expensive.

Then, just as I glanced out of the window, coming up the steps to enter the plane was the shocking pink, white-striped, cosy cushion, still clinging firmly to the neck of the little woman. When she entered and stopped in front of us, to hand over her boarding card to the cabin crew, my happy neighbour turned to me. 'Is she going for a swim?' he asked

To which I nearly choked trying to conceal my laughter. Keith just bent forward and checked that his life-jacket was in its place under the seat, just in case she knew something we didn't.

25

Little Treasures

Thursday afternoon was the weekly children's vaccine clinic and as usual this was fully booked with the first appointments of the afternoon taken up by the new babies and the later part of the clinic booked for the school children's booster injections. It was during one of these bookings that Robert, a five-year-old boy, attended for an appointment after school with his mum to have his school entry injections. As they entered my room the young man was somewhat bedraggled, knee socks around his ankles displaying a little pair of dirty knees, his school uniform was splattered with mud, and his tie was hanging over his shoulder, a picture of a typical playful schoolboy.

'I apologise for the state Robert is in,' said his mum.

'No problem,' I replied. 'He looks as if he has enjoyed his day at school.'

After his injection, which by the way had been administered without too much fuss, Robert turned to his mum as they prepared to leave and looking at her wide-eyed said, 'I won't come home dirty again, Mum, so I won't need any more needles.'

Poor little chap, he was convinced the vaccine was given as a punishment for getting dirty.

This reminded me of Bruce, the teenager who went to see his GP Dr Glaster at the surgery in Lanark, complaining of pain in his left ankle.

'Now let me have a look,' said the doctor, examining Bruce's swollen left foot. 'Can I see your other foot?'

'Well, Doctor, it's only my left foot that's sore,' Bruce hesitated.

'No, I need to see your right foot to be able to compare them,' said Dr Glaster.

Reluctantly Bruce took his right shoe and sock off and revealed a very dirty foot. 'Sorry, doctor, I did not know you would have to look at my good foot, I only washed the one.'

'Right,' said doctor, 'Go home and wash both your feet and when you have, come back and I will see you.'

Bruce limped out of the surgery with a very red face, before returning with two clean feet.

Dirty feet were not the problem when one late Tuesday morning the treatment room door burst open and a worried grandmother rushed in carrying her four-year-old grandson. The wee boy's pale face was tear-stained and his right hand was tied up with a large handkerchief. His anxious grandmother asked if I could help her by 'fixing' the child's hand.

'Let me have a look,' I replied.

I beckoned to her to sit down and hold the child while I untied the hanky, to check what the problem might be.

'What has happened?' I asked.

'He has had an accident, trapping his finger in the door,' continued his grandmother.

Expecting to find a cut or crushed finger I was shocked when undoing the covering I revealed his little hand with the top of his index finger missing.

'Oh dear, I can see the damage is quite severe,' I had to confess.

Without saying another word his grandmother handed me another handkerchief from her handbag. 'But can you fix it?' she asked.

Opening up the hanky she had just given me my mouth fell open as I sat looking at the top end of the little chap's finger lying cold and bloodless in the cotton wrap in my hand.

Quickly pulling myself together I collected some ice cubes from the treatment room fridge and carefully packing the precious digit in the ice before placing it into a container. I made the appropriate arrangements to have the child, who surprisingly was very quiet throughout the examination, to be taken with his grand-mother, who was carefully carrying the little container, to the Accident & Emergency unit at the hospital. Thankfully, within minutes they had gone.

The final outcome ended in a good result because thanks to the speed with which his poor shocked grandmother had brought him for help, combined with the speed and skill with which the team of doctors attended him on arrival at the hospital, they were successfully able to suture the little boy's finger part back. Eventually the nerve endings healed slowly and after several follow-up appointments at the hospital he was able to use his hand normally again in time.

Throughout life we all meet people whom we will never forget for whatever reason. One of these unforgettables was a four-year-old boy, Martin, brought in by his mother who had made an appointment with me requesting treatment for the burns that were sustained on the back of his legs. This little chap was so adorable, with his dirty face with clean streaks where his tears had washed away the grime: his tangled fair hair had not had a comb through it in some time, and his tee shirt and shorts displayed him as a real little ragamuffin, not too surprising since he did come from one of the more deprived areas on our list.

As I looked at this wee boy I knew this was one of the reasons I had gone into nursing in the first place, to be able to help people who trusted me to do so, and hopefully to make a difference to their medical situation and meet their needs. I found it easy to relate to Martin probably because he reminded me of my own childhood and background. I was puzzled at the position of the burns on his little legs, and although his mum explained that he had got them because he had stood too near a motorbike's exhaust pipe, I had my doubts. But I did not question the story because I was afraid I would lose her trust and Martin might not be brought back for treatment. However I did consult with the doctor on duty that day to express my concerns, and took his instruction to keep an eye on Martin.

Over the weeks that followed this little boy and I had some fun by making a game out of the treatment he had to have: this helped build a real trust between Martin and myself, and at the same time his legs healed and left no scars. One day during this time he arrived in the treatment room alone to have his dressings done. When I asked him who was with him, he told me his big sister had brought him to the surgery, before she had gone to the park (which was opposite the surgery) to play.

He went on to say he had got himself ready to come for his dressings to be changed. I have to say it was obvious the child had washed himself; the middle of his face was clean where the face cloth had been, and his hair around his face stood on end where the wet cloth had soaked it. He was wearing a sweater with a hole in the middle which showed his little tummy, and there he stood, looking up at me with a smile from ear to ear and holding a large rose in full bloom with its petals starting to shed. This he handed me with great delight.

I was so moved I could hardly speak; apparently he had taken the rose from someone's garden on the way to see me. I loved that little lad and looked forward to his visits. I was delighted his legs had healed, but I knew I would miss seeing his cheeky smile.

Sometimes the logic of children can surprise me and leave me wondering how they think things up. Little Ben was one of these little gems. He arrived with his mum Sophie who had an appointment with me: sadly Sophie was still grieving after the sudden death of her husband.

Being very aware of the sensitive situation I asked Sophie, when she had settled into the chair alongside my desk with young Ben hanging on to her arm afraid to let go, 'How are you and the family coping, Sophie?'

Before she could say anything little Ben answered for her with a positive, 'Daddy has just gone to Heaven, fishing.'

This was the natural reply from her seven-year-old son.

Sophie explained to me how her husband died while doing what he loved best – fishing.

A few appointments later Johnny, a five-year-old, was brought in to see me by his mum to have a splinter removed from his knee. Naturally the little boy was frightened and did not want me to touch his knee, so in an attempt to try to console her son his mum tried to take him mind off things and said, 'Tell Lynn it's your birthday tomorrow.'

'How old will you be Johnny?' I asked looking up.

'Six,' Johnny nervously answered.

'Oh! Are you married yet?' I laughingly asked.

'No!' says Johnny. 'I won't get married until I am 18 and then I'll go to Shrewsbury to get a wife.'

This was certainly a young man that knew what he wanted in life, and he had decided that the girls in Shrewsbury were obviously in his eyes a better class than those in Rosebank. All his thinking had taken his mind off the job in hand, and I managed to remove the offending splinter in no time and without any struggling from Johnny.

Now that Johnny had been attended to and had left my room quite happy, it was time to close down my computer and get ready for home. It was the end of yet another busy week and I was looking forward to the weekend ahead, so I was glad to see Keith pull up in the surgery car park to pick me up. We had just got as far as the railway bridge in Bendigo and as we turned the corner into Law Street we had to come to a sudden halt behind an ambulance that had been called to a road traffic accident.

A young boy coming home from school had just got off the bus and tried to dash across the road from behind the bus when a passing car had hit him, leaving the driver in shock and the boy unconscious. Apparently it had just happened minutes before we arrived. My first instinct was to get out of the car to ask if I could be of help: the ambulance crew knew me (there were no paramedics then) and asked if I would go with them to the hospital to help hold the boy steady as the journey was going to have to be a fast one.

In the back of the ambulance I tried to keep the boy on his

side, keeping his airways clear while the attendant dealt with the equipment. The driver took off for the 15-mile or so journey to the Royal Shrewsbury Hospital at high speed, not halting at anything that got in his way including red traffic lights. In fact he had to mount the kerb at the Rook Hotel lights in Minton in order to get past the cars that were in the way, the effects of which made the contents of the ambulance rattle around and made me reel as I had my hands occupied holding the child. The knock-on effect was that the attendant in turn grabbed me to prevent me bowling over. Keith followed in the car and managed to keep up without breaking the law.

At last we arrived at the hospital having completed the journey in record time thanks to the skills of the driver. The crew lost no time in quickly transporting the young boy straight to the intensive care unit and into the hands of the medical staff who were waiting. I also left the vehicle in a hurry, not in a rush to get home but, now suffering with travel sickness, I was embarrassed in case I was seen being unwell.

Keith and I headed home, concerned about the condition of the boy. He was not one of the patients on our surgery list: however it was pleasing to hear some days later that the little chap had made a complete recovery and was OK.

This accident reminded me about a tragic accident that happened to James, a boy who was in my class at the Lanark Grammar School in Scotland. He was about 11 or 12 years old and was on his way home from school with a crowd of his friends when he saw a lorry slowly driving up the narrow road in front of him. James could not resist the temptation to hitch a lift ran, jumped, and grabbed hold of the wood on the back of the lorry, lifting himself off the ground. The driver, unaware of having an unwanted passenger, gathered speed. Tragically James's belt from his gaberdine coat that he was wearing caught on the back wheel of the lorry and dragged him under, killing him instantly before the driver had a chance to do anything. This horrific scene was witnessed by all his friends and a good number of the school pupils on their way home; the whole school attended James's funeral, whose death was a great shock to the residents of Lanark.

Thankfully every car accident does not have to end in tragedy. There was one very fortunate little four-year-old boy who was carried into see me by his terrified mother. When Alex arrived, other than looking a little pale he appeared alright, where on the other hand his mum Pat looked terrible, and could not stop shaking with shock as she waited to hear the verdict of how her son was after he had been examined all over.

Apparently they were about to leave the house to go shopping and his mum had reversed the car down their driveway in preparation, intending to go back to the house to collect him. Instead she felt a bump and heard a yell from her son, who had gone behind the car, and could not be seen in the car mirror, causing her to run over him. The good thing about the whole thing was that the wheel of the car had not come in contact with Alex and he was too small for the undercarriage to have touched him as he lay on the ground.

In a state of panic Pat grabbed her son and drove to the surgery as quickly as she could to get help. As a precaution Alex was referred to the hospital to be checked over and was later discharged with no ill effects from his ordeal, and was soon running around as normal. However it took quite a while for his poor mother to get over the shock of what had happened, and the thought of what might have been the outcome of such an accident kept her awake at night for a long time.

Mishaps don't always occur when children are awake; one night Cathleen my niece, who was five years younger than me, would have choked to death had it not been for the quick action of her dad. She had been sucking a round, hard-boiled lollipop, the kind that changes colour the harder it's sucked. Cathleen and I had just finished our tea and were in the living room, while Jean (Cathleen's mum) was in the kitchen preparing John's dinner for him coming from work. Cathleen, who was only about three, was sitting in the big armchair next to the fire sucking her lollipop, and the combination of the warm room and the quietness made her drop off to sleep. I heard her making a funny noise and when I looked up at her she was cyanosed and the lollipop had disappeared. Just then John came in the door from work.

'Cathleen is a funny colour,' I said, running to him.

He took one look at her and could see the tip of the stick of the lollipop only just visible at the back of her throat. She had inhaled it as she slept. In seconds John with force pulled the lollipop out, which made a sound like a blocked drain being released as it left her throat.

He threw it on the fire and going into the kitchen angrily told Jean never to buy lollipops again. Jean was totally surprised, as the whole episode had happened all at once before she realised what he was talking about.

This was not to be the only time John came to the rescue to solve a problem that had happened to a family member. He came in one evening after a hard day's work to Helen crying her eyes out. She had not long had her ears pierced and fiddling had managed to push the butterfly back of her new earring inside the lobe of her ear, causing it to become inflamed, swollen and very painful. John took one look at her infected ear and without any warning used brute force to pull the front of the earring out of her lobe, dislodging the butterfly back attached to it.

Helen gave a yell and John threw the offending item on the fire, angrily telling her never to buy cheap earrings again. There was no danger of that, since it took some time before the swelling subsided enough for her to bear touching her ear, let alone poking any form of foreign objects in it.

26

Smoke-Free, Wart-Free and Fat-Free

When the Help to Quit Clinics were first introduced by the Primary Care Team (PCT) in Shropshire, their own nurse facilitator was sent to each GP surgery in their area to try and encourage each practice to implement their own clinics to meet the needs of their patients. The big incentive in doing so was not only a requirement by the government to address the health of the nation, but also the financial benefit to the individual practices if managed right.

Although the need for a non-smoking clinic in our practice had been suggested by one or two of our doctors prior to the PCT visit, I had always been reluctant to implement one, because as someone who had never smoked I felt inadequate to be able to talk to patients about stopping, and feared that the clinic would be a failure run by me. However, once the facilitator had provided our practice with set guidelines and protocols as to the form in which the clinics had to be delivered, alongside the support available at the end of a phone line and the provision of paperwork with the promise of ongoing study days and evenings, the only thing left for me to do was take up the challenge.

The patients who attended the early clinics were referred by the doctors who were treating them for a medical problem which they had presented with, and in many cases the problem was aggravated by smoking. Once the clinic was advertised within the practice the patients made their own self-referrals to seek help. After just a few weeks I felt quiet comfortable running this Help to Quit Clinic because I soon learnt that all I could really do was give the people the facts before piling on the support and encouragement. The rest was done by the patient, and their determination to succeed.

One day a young man who was a new patient to the practice came to see me. He wanted help to give up smoking, but while I was talking to him I had a feeling there was more than the eye could see.

'To enable me to help I need you to be completely honest with me,' I said.

As I looked into this man's face, he beamed from ear to ear as he replied, 'Oh, I really do want to stop smoking,' he said.

'You see, I am a Christian, and I need every aspect of my life to be clean,' he continued.

I was thrilled to hear this young man witness to me and told him I too was a Christian.

'Do you know the real meaning of why Jesus died for us?' he asked. 'Because we all have sinned and come short of the Glory of God,' he quoted.

He went on to chat how he would like to attend Bible School to enable him to extend his knowledge of the Bible to finally progress into the ministry.

As that young man left my room I felt uplifted after a busy difficult day, encouraged to know there was a fellow Christian out there motivated and enthusiastic to get on with the Lord's work. This young man's witness to me certainly had a positive effect: it made me wonder how much or how little effect my Christian witness had on my everyday living. This young man's visit left me with some serious thoughts about the many opportunities I failed to grasp in helping people cope better with their emotional feelings, which very often presented alongside their physical symptoms, and made me think, did I ever make any difference?

However, I must have been of some help to some of the patients who attended the Help to Quit Clinic that I implemented to support those who wanted to give up smoking. One young married man who worked in France faithfully made his follow-up appointment to see me last thing on a Friday afternoon, to allow him time to get from Birmingham Airport to Bendigo before the surgery closed its doors for the weekend. This man was so keen to stop smoking that he would frequently ring me up from the airport to apologise if he had to cancel his counselling because of a delayed flight. Before too long he had encouraged his wife to attend the clinic so that they could have a smoke-free home for their children to enjoy.

Each patient that came along to the clinic had a tale to tell and all had an excuse for smoking, but there was no doubt that none of the few hundred who had come over the years wanted to smoke; and for the many that had succeeded in stopping it was thrilling to see how delighted they were to be a non-smoker. I followed them up for a year before discharging them to allow me time for new patients to be seen.

The hours spent with these patients who were hooked on a habit that was without doubt damaging their health was well worth it, when I would often be rewarded for my efforts as I was walking on my way to work by perhaps the postman cycling down the hill and shouting to me, 'It's four years since I stopped.'

Or a van pulling up alongside me and an ex-smoker winding down the window to tell me, 'I haven't had one for two years now.'

It was comments like these that always amazed me but made me aware of the amount of encouragement needed and how important it was to support the patients in their time of need. The amazing thing was how much money most of the patients saved by stopping, and many put aside what they would normally have spent on cigarettes in a week to give themselves some incentive to achieve a much-desired goal in life. One couple sent me a postcard from Hawaii, saying how they were enjoying a smoke-free holiday with the money they would have blown away in the past: this was a great achievement for this particular man and wife since they had struggled financially in many aspects for their life in the past and hopefully now they would also enjoy better health in the future.

Others would tell me of the latest gadget they had managed

to purchase from their 'cigarette money': one man and wife re-decorated their home and furnished it anew to get rid of the smell of smoke, and intended to keep it smoke-free no matter who called to visit.

There was no age limit when it came to patients attending the clinic. One elderly man in his late seventies arrived saying he had started to smoke when he was seven: his aunt would send him to buy her Woodbines as there was no restriction on the age of purchase in those days, and as a reward she would give him a cigarette. I must admit I did have my doubts as to how success-ful this particular patient would be when it came to giving up: after all he had smoked all through the war and beyond, as he put it. So it was with great delight that eventually I was able to register this dear man as an ex-smoker after the first year of follow-up: but it was quite amusing to see him some months later still chewing his gum, even though it often got stuck in his den-tures, dislodging them as he spoke. Unembarrassed, he would put them straight before giving his usual grin and chewing on his way.

There were always the patients who would attend with the ex-pectation that I was going to perform some sort of magic to stop them from ever having another cigarette, with little or no effort coming from them to try and stop. I had a fair idea from their first visit whether or not they were really earnest about giving up: inevitably these were the people who would want to be pre-scribed the latest treatment they had seen advertised, or that a friend had sworn by, irrelevant if it was suitable for their indi-vidual health or lifestyle. The choice of prescribed treatments de-pended on the patient's health needs, as some of the side-effects from the items suited some but were not advised for others.

However there was always something certain, and that was if an individual was determined enough to stop smoking he or she would manage to, no matter how many failed attempts they had before finally reaching their goal. It is difficult to believe, but it is a medical fact that it is easier to stop a heroin addiction than a nicotine one, even though many smokers will say, 'I can stop if I want to.' If this was the case there would be no need for Help to Quit Clinics in the first place.

Another of the services the practice decided to provide for the patients was a cryogenic clinic. This was where by using a liquid nitrogen cylinder the nurses could freeze off unwanted 'extras' that patients presented with and requested to have removed. In the past such cases would have been referred to Outpatients at the hospital and apart from the inconvenience caused by the individual having to wait for a hospital appointment, the hospital appointment system was getting clogged up with minor ailments which could be addressed in a GP surgery. The 'extras' consisted of such things as warts, verrucas, skin tags or blemishes in the form of certain moles depending on the texture or severity as each case was examined and referred on to the nurse accordingly. The clinic was held every two weeks for no longer than two hours in an afternoon because the liquid nitrogen which had to be collected from a neighbouring surgery at the last minute only had a short existence before it evaporated. This meant that each clinic was usually well attended, and due to follow-up appointments from the existing patients being treated new patients sometimes found it difficult to get fitted in.

Because the clinic was on an afternoon there was normally a large attendance of school pupils lining up to have their unwanted wart or verruca removed, and after the first visit when they discovered that the procedure was not painful only very cold they would recommend it to their friends, who often presented with the least little problem just to try out what it was all about. The good thing about the clinic was that we were able to treat the junior pupils and get rid of their sometimes many verrucas without causing them pain in doing so.

Then there were the adults who attended in the hope of losing their unsightly mole that had been with them for years. Such was the case when I was treating numerous moles on the back of a very large patient, who was sitting legs astride a chair with his bare back facing me when there was a knock at the door and Carol the healthcare assistant walked in to the sight of an ample bare belly, which took her by surprise.

'Oh! I am sorry, I wanted to ask you something,' she said.

'It's OK, I am only spraying the garage door,' I laughed, holding the liquid nitrogen cylinder.

'Thank you very much,' smiled the good-natured patient with a frozen back.

Who, by the way, continued to keep his appointment every two weeks for a touch-up job until he had had his moles removed, and felt comfortable if he took his shirt off while fishing. He was a keen fisherman, and spent a lot of time outdoors in the summer, exposing his bare back to the rays of the sun by removing his shirt, Although, now he had been made more aware of the health risks with the sun effects on his skin, he decided he would be more careful in the future.

Attending for a cryogenic appointment, Sarah presented with numerous skin tags around her neck and asked if they could be removed. After discussing the procedure with her, and explaining that it might take several follow-up appointments to complete the task, she decided to opt for the alternative treatment which involved tying each skin tag off at the base with a surgical suture thread, cutting off the blood supply and causing them to drop off after a few days. The downside meant that each tie-off pinched the skin. Sarah tolerated having the left side of her neck treated but found that the stinging feeling was too much to continue to have the right side of her neck tag-free on the same appointment, so she would make another later.

Sarah left the room with what resembled 16 dead flies attached to the left side of her neck and an equal amount of skin tags on the right side which she concealed under a long scarf until she could return in two weeks' time. At her next appointment she was delighted with the result after the suture threads had fallen off leaving her with a smooth left side to her neck, and was prepared to endure the same to have the right side looking as good.

In time it did, and Sarah's self-esteem also improved, since she had put up with the embarrassment of having so many skin tags for quite a long period of time, but now she had no need always to wear a scarf to try and hide them.

Another clinic that improved patients' self-esteem as well as helping to benefit their health in the long term was the Weight Clinic, although I have to confess that when it was first suggested by the GPs that the nurses should implement one into the weekly work-load, my heart sank. I knew of patients who had been on the list for years, and for years had been overweight despite the health advice they had been given by either a nurse or doctor during one of their frequent visits for another problem.

Nevertheless, perhaps a proper structured clinic would be the answer? I was willing to give it a try, and set aside time for such a clinic. There was little need to advertise the Weight Clinic within the practice, because my colleagues and the GPs were only too eager to refer their obese patients, as no one finds it an easy or quick treatment, and results are normally slow to achieve. The positive side to the clinic was that there was no shortage of patients willing to attend in the hope of having some magic overnight cure, but with sheer willpower on their part and buckets full of encouragement on my part, sometimes amazing things did occur.

One of the first patients to book her appointment was a young lady called Vicky who had just registered at the practice, having recently moved into the area from Stoke-on-Trent. She had not yet made many friends, but had arrived with the intention of giving herself a fresh start in life. She hoped to obtain a new image now that she was living in a new environment, so her first port of call had been the surgery in an attempt to get her fit. I was in the reception area when she was making her enquires about the clinic, so the receptionist called me over to have a word with Vicky.

'How can I help?' I asked.

'My husband has bought me a new dress and it is a size too small,' said Vicky in a voice so loud that it caught the attention of the patients sitting in the waiting room, making them stop talking to each other and listen – especially the regulars who did not know this new resident of Bendigo.

'I see, and the reason he has done that is . . .' I waited.

'So that it will encourage me to lose weight,' said she.

'Well, I am sure I might be able to help you if you want to come and see me in clinic.'

'Yes, I'm determined to get into that dress,' emphasised Vicky. 'I have hung it on the outside of my wardrobe so that I see it everyday to remind me,' she said, having now received her appointment card.

As Vicky left the surgery I was aware that perhaps this Weight Clinic was going to be more demanding than I first thought, if Vicky was anything to go by. She was grossly overweight, to the extent that when she did attend her first few visits, I had to ask her to get weighed at the hospital prior to coming for counselling because the practice scales limit was 20 stone, and therefore unable to accommodate Vicky, who was 23 stone initially.

Over the weeks and the many appointments that Vicky attended, she would tell me tales about the things that were happening in her life, some of which I never knew whether they were true or not. One week she came in with a large box of cream cakes perched on the top of her full shopping bag.

After I had attended to her and found that there was no reduction in her weight from the previous week, I glanced at the box of cakes and asked, 'What have you got here, Vicky?'

Without turning a hair Vicky replied, 'Well you see I have some visitors from Stoke and they have taken over my house. I can't get them out and I am having to feed them: the cakes are not for me.'

'Are you sure?' I could only smile.

Some weeks into the programme Vicky arrived proudly wearing her new dress taken from the hanger outside the wardrobe, although to many onlookers it might have still appeared to be too tight. But that did not matter: both Vicky and I knew she had achieved her goal by getting her weight down into the teens.

Many of the patients who attended the Weight Clinic had been referred by a doctor because it was found that they had health issues and their weight was part of the underlying problem. Each had a goal in mind for their own personal reasons: one girl had been referred to the hospital to have an operation to reduce her very large breasts which were causing her to suffer with chronic backache, and the surgeon had instructed her to lose a specific amount of weight before he would consider carrying out the breast reduction.

Another man had to address his weight problem because his diabetes was out of control; another had unfortunately had his first heart attack and was told by the physicians to adapt a healthier lifestyle in order to help reduce his cholesterol levels – altering his diet was high on the list.

Others had their own goals that they hoped to achieve for their own reasons. The most difficult part I had to play in my role was to keep their motivation going, especially with the patients who had struggled for years, trying every fashionable diet available. It was a fact that the male patients seemed to have more willpower when it came to sticking to healthy eating than a number of the female patients: whether it was a macho thing or the fear of getting on the scales and finding they had failed, I don't know, but it appeared to be the case.

One person that comes to mind as being a great success was Charlie. He was a jolly farmer who had been told by the doctor that his blood pressure was elevated, and that he would need to take regular medication to treat it. In addition he was asked to reduce his weight. Charlie and his family had been patients at the surgery for years, and he had appeared, along with his family, to have good health: on the odd occasion that any of them had attended the surgery it had usually been for some routine procedure such as tetanus vaccination cover, or perhaps advice or treatment for a minor incident that had occurred on the farm. I had known his wife from the Antenatal Clinic, and the children who now had left college and were working had been given all their children's vaccines by me in the past.

There was no doubt that Charlie had taken on board the advice given by the doctor and was determined to do his best by complying with the treatment; the difficulty lay in the practical side of the work he did. As a farmer his day started early and this could mean that he was out in the fields on his tractor all day, so packed snacks were the normal routine and needed to be adequate to give him the energy he required to do his job. The second problem for him was getting to the surgery (which was a distance from the farm) at a time that was practical for him and that suited surgery opening hours. These were minor things that between us we sorted out: as long as Charlie was willing to attend for treatment I was able to be flexible and fit him in on the first early morning appointment. Within a short period of time Charlie had not only reduced his weight sufficiently, but he told me he had also saved money by resisting the chocolate and snack bars on the counter in his local village shop each morning when he called to buy his daily newspaper, an action that did not please the newsagent, although he had been impressed by the visible weight loss that Charlie had achieved and told him so.

Over the months some won the battle, others continued to struggle. Ultimately it was agreed between the medical staff that the most efficient way to address the problem, especially with the patients who were either reluctant or found it difficult to attend the Weight Clinic, would be to abolish the set clinic and in doing so release the allocated appointment time for other issues, and that each professional should just incorporate promoting a healthier lifestyle to the individuals concerned when they attended the practice for other appointments.

This proved to be a reasonable decision because there were more and more WeightWatchers and other such classes being set up in and around the Bendigo area, at times and places that could be better for people to get to after work. Some of our patients who went to these classes found that being with others and sharing ideas helped to keep them motivated in achieving their goal.

27

The Joy of Hospital Visiting

I think it is fair to say that not many of us enjoy hospital visiting. Apart from the obvious concerns we may have about the patients who are in hospital whether it be friend or family, there are the day in, day out hours of visiting and wondering what we can find to talk about to help lift the spirits of the poor person that has to be there against their will.

Unfortunately over recent years my sister Margaret has had her fair share of hospital admissions and sometimes for many weeks at a time. Despite this she has never complained or asked, 'Why me?' even though on several occasions she has been very ill and had to be admitted as an urgent medical case. As a Christian she trusted in The Lord and found comfort in His word, as it says in Isaiah 55 verse 8: 'For My thoughts are not your thoughts, nor are My ways your ways.' So whenever she felt well enough throughout her stay in hospital, she would help those around her and endeavoured to cheer them along with her sense of humour.

In return she would be entertained at certain times by some of the various visitors that were attending their own loved one in the neighbouring bed to Margaret. One afternoon the patient next to her in the ward had a visit from her son who, like Margaret, liked to tease his mother and try to bring a bit of fun to the other patients around: that is, to those who felt like it. The young man came in sat by his mother's bed and removed his shoe and promptly put it to his ear before saying 'Hello' and again, 'Hello.' Then, continuing once he had the attention of the other patients, 'Hello, is that you, Shoey?'

His mother nudged him to make him behave himself, to which he took no notice. Then a nurse came into the ward to make up a new bed ready for the next admission, and as she crossed the room to the bed in question, the young man got up from his chair and tried to squeeze into his mother's flowery dressing gown. Having managed to get the gown on he walked over to the nurse and asked her if his bed was ready. The nurse, who had seen him on several previous visits, was familiar with his actions and laughingly threatened him to behave.

Visitors like him helped to lighten the otherwise long days for some patients who on some days had no visitors themselves and were glad of a bit of entertainment to break up the monotony of just waiting for the next meal or procedure depending on what came first.

Visiting time was over at the Royal Hospital as I hurried from the ward where I had been visiting Margaret, in an attempt to catch the bus that I could see waiting at the stop in the hospital grounds. Normally I would have taken my car and paid the two pound car parking fee at the hospital, but it was a lovely after- noon and as the bus ran every 15 minutes from Bendigo to the hospital, plus the fact that I was now the proud owner of a free blue bus pass, I had decided to go by public transport.

Just as I approached the bus stop the bus pulled away. Waiting at the stop was Hazel (a patient registered at the practice), who had just been visiting her husband Ralph in hospital. Ralph had been fitted with a new pacemaker for his heart condition some years earlier, but unfortunately he had suffered a long illness over the recent years, and at this time was very ill in hospital.

'How are you, Hazel?' I asked.

'Oh, I am OK. It's Ralph that's not so good,' replied Hazel.

'I am so sorry to hear your husband is so ill,' I sympathised.

'Yes,' said this tired lady. 'The trouble is his pacemaker keeps kick starting him.'

Straight away I had this mental vision of dear Ralph lying in a hospital bed like Black Bess, my old banger from the past, with the bonnet up being recharged from an another old banger nearby. But that was just my vivid imagination and sense of humour, and fortunately for me my bus pulled up and I was able to make my escape before I put my foot in it by making some comment that might not go down well with poor Hazel at that point.

After Margaret had endured several weeks in the Royal Hospital with little improvement to her health, the medical team decided that she would have to be transferred to the Hartlands Hospital in Birmingham to have further tests and probably another operation carried out in the hope of getting her well enough to enable her to come home.

This was the first time she had ever been in the Hartlands and travelling to Birmingham to visit was a new experience to the rest of the family as no one was familiar with the area. But it was indeed a rather frightening experience for Margaret in particular, who had to share a hospital bay where the patient in the next bed to her was a convicted prisoner and was chained to the policeman who had the job of guarding the inmate while he was a patient there. As visitors we were also alarmed by the sight of the long chain that accompanied the prisoner up and down the hospital corridor as he made his way to the food trolley to collect his meal, or to the bathroom dragging behind him his officer in charge.

The sight of the officer sitting next to Margaret was of little comfort to her as she lay there at night hearing the clanging of the convict's heavy chain as he turned and tossed in his bed; her health seemed to deteriorate, not helped by the anxiety of the situation. Fortunately she never did find out what crime this young fellow had committed, but it was fair to say that one would imagine that he was certainly not a very well person to have been admitted to that hospital unit, although looking at him he appeared physically fit and his movements did not seem restricted or painful.

Nevertheless, after yet more weeks of everyone having to travel through the busy traffic on their way to Birmingham, it was pleasing to see Margaret reach a level of fitness sufficient for her to be discharged and come back to the comfort of her own home.

The family, as well as she, hoped they would not have to visit the Hartland Hospital again; however this was not to be dismissed, as we were soon to discover when yet another Dickie member came to England and stayed longer than first planned.

It was not surprising that my nephew Wilson, having been born into the Dickie family, developed into a natural comedian – as most of the Dickies are known by anyone coming in contact with them to be a little mad. However Wilson's humour was soon put to the test when he decided to travel with a friend from Scotland to Birmingham for a short holiday. This alone makes one wonder who in their right mind would leave the beauty of the Clydeside where he lived to the glamour of the skyscrapers in Birmingham for a holiday. Nevertheless an unexpected break is what he got, for while Wilson was out in Birmingham with his friends on the Saturday night, he slipped and fell flat on his back as he ran trying to stop a taxi.

His friends thought it was funny seeing him lie there, but only until they realised he could not get up and that he was not on this occasion acting the fool. As they rallied round and got Wilson to his feet they soon discovered he could not support himself because he had no feeling in his legs, and he knew by this that he had injured his back. Without delay Wilson's friends soon called 999 and he was taken by ambulance to the Casualty unit at the Hartlands Hospital. Keith and I found him there the next morning, after receiving a phone call from Richard in Scotland, worried about his son's condition and anxious because this was Wilson's first experience as a patient; he was a complete novice when it came to hospitals.

This had been made clear to all the family months earlier when he went to visit his sister Susan who was a patient in the Wishaw General in Scotland and as Wilson wandered in and out of the wards a nurse, conscious of security, stopped him and asked him who he was.

Wilson, who apart from being anxious about his sister's welfare was nervous and missed the question, replied. 'Susan.'

'You don't look like a Susan to me,' the nurse said, much to Wilson's embarrassment as he quickly corrected himself.

'No, that's my sister's name.'

So hospitals and Wilson just did not come easy: he had no idea what to expect, let alone how to modify his broad Scottish accent so that the Brummies could understand him.

When we found Wilson he was lying in Casualty with his feet hanging out the end of the bed, not unusual as after all he was 6 foot 4 inches long, but looked even longer lying down. However it was some time before, he discovered we were there because he was still sleeping, exhausted after the happenings of the night before not to mention the affects of the alcohol he consumed before the fall.

Wilson had been X-rayed on admission to Casualty and once the results showed he had fractured some discs in his lower back, he was transferred from Casualty to the spinal unit where he had to lie flat on his back until the consultants decided on treatment.

Being a patient was an ordeal for Wilson, not helped by the added pressure of having to lie flat and unable to get up to go to the toilet. After a few days the nurses on his ward tried in vain to persuade Wilson to use a bed pan.

'No, I am not going to the toilet in this bed,' he insisted.

Eventually one nurse pulled the screen around his bed and, holding his big Scottish hand, assured him it was her job to attend to his needs, and that she had seen it all before.

'No, I am not going in this bed,' repeated Wilson.

The nurse, trying her utmost to encourage him to comply, suggested, 'We could wheel your bed out on to the fire escape for you to go if you like.'

'Great,' said Wilson to himself, 'I don't want the embarrassment of going to the toilet in the ward, so they will put me outside for the rest of the world to see me perform.'

Now whether or not it was the fear of being put on display to the rest of the population in Birmingham, or not, nobody knows, but eventually natural functions resumed as normal much too everyone's relief, especially Wilson's.

After a week and a lot of effort on Wilson's part trying to get himself mobile, the consultant decided that with the aid of a specially fitted harness, which had to be made to measure, Wilson would be able to travel back to Scotland where arrangement had been made for his treatment to be continued. When Richard and Margaret (his mum and dad) received this information, they made the journey to Birmingham to take Wilson home, and as they arrived on the ward to collect him the one nurse who had spent some time nursing Wilson threw her outstretched arms in the air as Wilson was leaving and shouted, 'Freedom!'

The nurse had seen the film *Braveheart* staring Mel Gibson who played the part of William Wallace, and she was imitating the Scottish hero William Wallace when he fought against the English to gain Scotland's freedom. Witnessing this display of humour, Richard and Margaret knew there was no doubt that Wilson had left his own mark on Birmingham, especially with the nursing staff and the patients who had shared his company for the relatively short time he was there.

Wilson was not the only one who made a lasting impression on the hospital staff he left behind. John attended surgery for his routine six-week injection and while I administered the treatment prescribed for him, he told me the outcome of his recent visit to the Royal Hospital in Minton. John's right thumb had caused him some pain over a period of time and after being checked several times by the GP was thought to have minor problems. He had been referred by the doctor to the surgeon for a second opinion and the procedure had been explained to him by the GP as a fairly simple operation.

At the hospital the surgeon examined John's right thumb and nodded. 'Yes I can fix this,' he went on to explain. 'I would have to amputate from the base,' he said, studying John's hand. 'Let's see the left thumb while you are here.'

John stunned into silence, lifted his left hand for the surgeon to examine.

'Yes, this looks like it would be better off as well. We'll see when we have you under.'

Before the doctor could finish what he was saying, John took to his heels and ran, not stopping until he reached his car, shouting over his shoulder as he fled, 'I don't think so.'

Leaving the consultant amused.

'How did I get into that situation?' John asked me.

'Was the surgeon foreign?' I enquired.

'Yes' said John, who had served in the war, then as an afterthought he uttered, 'German, I think.'

John to this day is the proud owner of two thumbs.

28

Closing the Doors

The build-up of anticipation about moving to a new surgery started weeks before the actual due date; because we were going to be moving out of Hill Street it was first thought that perhaps we should think about giving the practice a new name for its new location. With this idea circulated amongst the population of the surgery the suggestions came in fast and furious: some were too daft to mention but each person who came up with a name hoped theirs would be chosen, convinced it was the best.

An elderly gentleman came into see me one day and during his consultation he mentioned that changing the name of the surgery was not a very good idea. 'After all, the Boweryhill name has a lot of local history,' he said.

Apparently The Boweryhill, referred to as a miniature Tinto, was a 200,000-ton pit-mound, the biggest of 200 similar disfigurements near Bendigo. It loomed menacingly over the railway bridge and memorial gates of Dandez Park, casting a shadow, and it was blocking the expansion of the town. Work started on 14th July 1933 to remove it, work that had been inspired by the Reverend J.E. Brigend, the vicar of St Lukes Church.

The site was given as a voluntary gift by the Tinto Brewery Company, the clerk to the council and the surveyor gave their services free; this was a time when the industries of Bendigo had gradually disappeared with none being replaced. The scheme helped boost morale when unemployment was rife and spirits were low because the Depression was hitting hard. Fourteen members of the International Voluntary Services for Peace (IVSP) and their leader (a son of a former President of The Swiss Republic) who started the IVSP movement in 1920, were the first to dig.

The Boweryhill scheme was the subject of many arguments as to who should have the site, at first it was proposed that new council offices be put there, but in 1936 other property was purchased. As a result of a grant being refused towards the levelling, the Bendigo 'Mountain of Friendship' came to a standstill in 1938. When the committee had recovered from the shock they started clearing a site for a bus terminus and car park, and £250 was granted by the council, then another £100 was needed to complete the roadside scheme, but this was rejected by the council. So an appeal for funds was launched to complete the work, proposed by Revd Brigend: the IVSP offered its services in order that this might be accomplished. The first piece of land levelled was used to provide a space for the huts for the unemployed; after several years of hard work the site for the bus terminus was complete.

Now the space housed the Boweryhill Surgery and a home for the elderly – – Brigend House, named after Revd Brigend, the man who had organised the scheme.

Knowing the history of the Boweryhill had a great impact, and at a given opportunity the doctors were informed that the change of name might be upsetting to some of our elderly patients, apart from being confusing to others including neighbouring practices and the different health disciplines that we dealt with regularly. After consideration it was decided not to change the name.

The last week after 34 years at the Boweryhill Surgery was all hustle and bustle with each member of staff trying to clear their rooms and pack up their books, paperwork, and individual items into boxes which they sealed and clearly marked with the number of the room they would have in the new building; this procedure was carried out between seeing patients. The difficulty was to know what could be packed and what would be needed right up until the final patient had been seen. The doctors' and nurses' appointments were booked right up until lunchtime on the Friday, leaving the afternoon free to complete the packing. The good thing about clearing one's room is that it gives one a chance to dispose of the unused items that are no longer needed but have lain tucked away in a cupboard, taking up much-needed space over a period of years.

Everyone had the same idea, which was to start work in the new surgery with new equipment and not take along any tatty or unnecessary junk that might spoil the new image that we intended to portray. The patients' appointments on the last week at the old surgery had been fully booked in advance, with the majority of patients anxious to find out if there would be any changes to the normal routine of the practice; some patients asked if there would be new doctors at the new surgery.

'No, they do not come with new buildings,' I replied.

However, most of the patients were excited about the move to such an impressive building and thrilled at the idea of a large patients' car park, something that had been a disadvantage for many years at Hill Street where patients struggled to find a car space on the street; the residents living in Hill Street were not sorry to see the cars go: now at last their street would be available for the cars of their friends and family to park in.

Once the surgery closed the doors to appointments on the Friday afternoon, the staff started to take what they could carry up to the new premises and set to arranging their individual consulting rooms ready for work on the following Monday. While they were busy unloading their boxes (which had managed to be delivered to the right rooms) and placing their items in the new beech wood office furniture, Peter (the practice manager) and myself made a last visit to the old Boweryhill Surgery to have a final check on the premises to make sure nothing had been left behind that might be wanted in the future.

As we wandered around the abandoned building, in and out of the now empty rooms, it was difficult to imagine the passage of people that had walked along the corridor over the many years. The characters who had walked through the surgery doors were not only the patients who attended for treatment but also the staff who had the pleasure of serving them. Each staff member had something or other happening in their lives; so it was with Lizzy, one of our first receptionists, who told me what had happened to her a few years previously.

One night while she and her husband were asleep in bed in their cottage in the country she woke with the feeling of being dragged down the bed by her ankle. In her sleepy state her natural reaction was to put her arms around her husband's waist in an attempt to hold on. This pulling action of holding on caused her husband to wake, finding Lizzy now shaking and screaming in terror saying she could see a man standing at the bottom of the bed holding her ankle. Baxter her husband put on the light as he reassured her it was only a dream. However, it took him some time to settle Lizzy, who still insisted she could see the man even with the light on. After constant reassurance from her husband she eventually settled back to try and sleep.

Many months later Lizzy and hubby moved from that house, and one evening while they were hosting a dinner party in their new home, the topic of conversation turned to dreams and happenings experienced in the past. This led Lizzy to relate the horrific dream she had had in her old home, about the man holding on to her ankle. Only then did her husband say that the most awful thing about the whole night was that when he put on the light he also could see the form of a man holding Lizzy's leg. After what seemed like an age, he vanished. Lizzy was astonished now she knew for the first time that it had not been her imagination. Of course if her husband had told her at the time that he too could see someone she would have been too frightened to stay in the house a moment longer. So he kept quiet until he could find them somewhere else to live.

Lizzy experienced another scary moment one early morning while in bed in the old house, when the neighbour's cat jumped through the open bedroom window, landing on the sleeping Lizzy's chest. Surviving what could have been a heart attack, her sheer fright made Lizzy grab the cat, rush downstairs, and without hesitation throw the animal out of the front door, never to return – at least not in the time they had left in that house.

Cats played a part in the life of yet another earlier receptionist. Dot loved cats so much that one lunchtime she bought two kittens which she could not resist as she passed the pet shop window in Bendigo where they were playing. Having brought them back to the surgery she smuggled them in rather than leave them in the car, and kept them in a box under the appointment desk until the end of surgery some four hours later. Needless to say the doctors who were in their consultant rooms had no knowledge of this, and were puzzled why, when on the odd occasion throughout the afternoon that they came into the reception area, the staff there would gather in a huddle to conceal the box, and chat so that the mews from the kittens could not be heard.

One week later Dot discovered she had fleas in the house and no matter what she tried no flea deterrent made any difference. It was suggested by her colleagues, who did not fancy sharing her flea bites, that perhaps she should contact the council to fumigate her new carpets, in case that was where they were coming from. As a last resort she did contact the council, who said they would be along to see her shortly, but the council being the council meant at their convenience.

The following morning Dot with several of the staff was at the reception desk, attending to the very busy influx of patients, when two council men arrived. Pushed for time the council men called over the heads of the patients waiting at the desk, 'Who is the lady with the fleas?'

'She is!' shouted all the staff at once, pointing to Dot.

After the council's visit to Dot's home the fleas were found to have come from her new carpets, which were duly fumigated, and not the kittens.

Perhaps cats and surgeries go together because when I called

250

to see a colleague at a neighbouring surgery, there in the entrance of the practice sat a black and white cat next to an empty dish. I could not make up my mind if the cat was waiting for a passer-by to throw a coin in the dish or a piece of fish; whatever he was expecting, he just sat and waited. As I was leaving the practice I stopped to have a chat to the cat, much to the amusement of a rather large Jamaican lady coming out of the surgery after seeing a doctor. The cat, not so amused, took one look at me then one look at the weather which was in the throes of a real downpour, and decided to take the latter option and dived out in the rain, leaving me with the empty dish.

However, I was not the only crazy nurse when it came to dealing with cats. I once worked alongside a practice nurse who had a cat that according to her could turn on the water tap when it decided to have a drink while she was at work. The nurse never thought it was a tall tale to swallow and never hesitated to tell colleagues how clever her cat was, and could not understand why they smiled in doubt and disbelief.

And now the deserted building echoed at the sound of our footsteps and conversation as we looked at the bits and pieces that were no longer required and had been left discarded in various corners of the rooms. Yes, this place of work had seen so many events take place over the years, and had a history, some of which would never be forgotten by those who had been part of it. Over the years there were many who had joined the surgery team: some just seemed to pass through, others stayed a little longer. As they departed to seek new adventures either at home or abroad, they each left behind their own impressions on the people they had worked with.

One fleeting doctor who stayed briefly, was Dr Jeffs a young GP who had previously spent a time in Australia back packing. He would arrive to start his morning surgery wearing his favoured rucksack, then after the morning appointments he would carry out his home visits attending to the patients, rummaging in his well-travelled bag to find the required implements needed in treating the somewhat puzzled individuals who waited in expectation to see what this unusual GP would draw from his bag.

Dr Jeffs certainly had very different ideas of working in a GP practice, compared to his predecessors or indeed our current partners; he would spend a great deal of time in the building checking up on what the clerical staff got up to during their working hours, and did not hesitate to approach certain members to question their value in the workplace. Eventually the wanderlust took him over and he bade his farewells, picked up his rucksack and left, leaving a shortfall in the number of doctors necessary to serve a growing practice population adequately. This gap was to be filled by an attractive young female doctor who had flown over from her GP practice in Canada to visit her ageing parents who lived on the outskirts of Rosebank.

Dr Burton, whose home county had been Shropshire, was married with two teenagers who were still attending college in Canada. She had enquired about GP vacancies within Shropshire with the intention of moving the family here and Bowery-hill. Surgery was fortunate to obtain her even if it was, as it turned out, to be only for a short period. She fitted in with the practice and the staff as one who had always been there, and brought with her many good methods that she soon adapted and applied, moulding them to suit the needs of the patients she was now seeing. Her pleasant personality and energy were an inspiration to both staff and colleagues alike, who found it refreshing to have her on board our team.

Unfortunately, her own family found it difficult to adapt to the very different lifestyle that Shropshire had to offer, especially her teenagers, who missed their friends in Canada; as a result Dr Burton regrettably waved us goodbye and moved back to Canada.

Following her departure several locum doctors helped with the workload, but one stayed and later decided to become a partner. The first time I saw the new locum was one morning after seeing one of the consulting room doors open and a young man coming out, wearing a tomato-red blazer. If it had not been for that bright jacket I would probably never have given him a second glance as he walked into the reception area carrying a bundle of patients' notes on his way to return them to the receptionist to file.

'Who is that new doctor?' I asked Stella.

'That's our new locum cover, Dr Field, he's a real hoot,' she laughed.

If ever there was an unconventional GP he was. In his own time his hobby was painting and he fancied himself as an artist, and it showed in the way he dressed with his very colourful patterned shirts, from the Flower Power era; later when he joined as a partner he would hang his art work (usually painting of local scenes) around his consulting room, in the hope that perhaps someone might wish to purchase one. I have to admit some pictures were quite good.

One afternoon a patient, coming from Dr Field's room, stopped and asked me, 'Can I have one of those shirts that Dr Field wears on a prescription?'

'Sorry, I am afraid they are only unique to him.'

During Dr Field's time at the Bowerhill medical surgery, he remarried and confused us all by changing his name to Dr Butter-Field; at first this made the patients think we had another new doctor join the practice until they realised that no two people would wear shirts like that. His shirts matched his personality – full of fun.

Then the last recruit was Dr Amber, a female doctor who had been a GP for a number of years at another practice just outside the Rosebank area and had decided on a change of scenery. In order to help with the transaction the partners decided to invite her out for an evening meal as a means of getting to know them, and asked me to join them at the Sugar Loaf in Thiston.

On arrival at the restaurant I was introduced to Dr Amber and we were placed to sit next to each other at the dining table. We got on well and chatted about the practice, and I answered any questions she might have. Then to the surprise of the other doctors after a few glasses of wine I told her what her new partners were like to work with, working my way around the table in humour I let her know what to expect from each of them: together we shared a lot of laughter throughout the evening, and a few secrets.

The following morning back at work Dr Cummingham warned me, 'After last night if Dr Amber does not take the job it will be your fault.'

'No worries, she'll come.'

And come she did, bringing her skills with her, and was also prepared to join in with the fun created by the staff, eager to make her feel part of the team. We were ready for new surroundings, because now this once state-of-the-art building now looked old, worn and tired in the light of our new practice in Hope Street. It was now time to move on and leave the past behind, but perhaps take the experience gained and the lessons learnt as I endeavoured to hopefully provide a better service for the population on our list. Peter turned the key in the lock for the last time at the Boweryhill Surgery in Hill Street and we walked away and headed for our new renamed, Built Boweryhill Surgery in Hope Street, 500 yards up the road in Bendigo.

BBC Radio Shropshire were waiting to interview us about our expectations for the new premises, but although we were well aware that a building can have an influence in bringing about change, it is the people working within the building that really have to bring about the real change to be able to meet the needs of the patients we aim to help.

29

The New Surgery

There was still a great deal to be done at the new Boweryhill Surgery in Bendigo, which was three months late on opening due to building delays, but finally the state-of-the-art surgery serving 10,000 residents opened on the 15th September 2003 after a weekend of furniture being wheeled in and computers being installed ready for the patients.

That weekend the practice moved from its outgrown premises into better, bigger facilities built on derelict land opposite the railway station in Bendigo, the building conspicuous with its red walls, green windows and large grey pillars. Now patients have a much-needed car park, and automatic doors into the £1 million-plus premises.

Within the building, doors are of a wheelchair friendly width and there is a lift to the first floor to offices, more treatment rooms, a children's clinic, consulting rooms and a purpose-built minor surgery room where GPs can remove lumps and bumps along with various minor procedures that otherwise might have needed a hospital appointment in the past.

Within the same building the final touches were also being made to a Lloyds Pharmacy as product codes were scanned into the system ready for trade. This modern pharmacy has a consultation area which will allow the pharmacist to offer diabetic screening and blood pressure tests which were not available on the old site. Having a pharmacy located adjacent to the health centre is part of the government policy to have these one-stop centres, and hopefully the patients would find this convenient in terms of prescriptions dispensed. Also the closer working relationship between the GPs and pharmacy would allow any queries to be resolved more quickly; also being co-located may mean that some patients instead of seeing the doctor about advice on their medication might ask the pharmacist and in doing so perhaps shift some of the pressure away from the doctor so that they only see patients that they need to see.

Now that we had moved into the new premises the doctors had every intention of only seeing the patients they needed to see, and to be able to do this the reception staff were instructed to fill the nurses' appointments first with any patient that required a nursing procedure or a problem that a nurse could deal with. The nurse, knowing her capabilities, would refer the patient on to the GP if necessary or if the patient had a heath issue that only the doctor should deal with. With this appointment system in place the theory was that more doctors' appointments should be available for the patients that needed to be seen by them; however in general practice patients are seen by the nurse in various ways:

- by self-referral when by their own choice they want to see a nurse;
- by referral from a receptionist when they phone or arrive and need to be seen by someone;
- by referral from the GP who considers it something that can be carried out by a nurse, or in the case of a follow-up appointment.

Because of the variety of ways that a patient was able to see a nurse, the nurses' appointments were invariably full at the start of the day; this had also occurred in the old premises as patients were made aware of the extent of treatments the nurses were able to carry out for them. The demand to see the nurse was even greater now with the new premises: it would appear that everyone wanted to come and have a look at what was now on offer in such a grand setting, and the overflow of patients had to be sent to see the doctors.

But given the choice, nine out of ten patients would usually prefer to see a doctor rather than a nurse for obvious reasons; mainly to give them peace of mind, knowing that a doctor should know the cause of their problem that they presented with and, more importantly, be able to cure them of it or refer them on to someone who could.

Along with the changes to the appointment system came the end of the emergency Saturday morning surgery, and although the cut in hours was welcomed by the GPs, the patients on the receiving end of such changes were not so happy, especially those who were in the habit of calling in on the offchance of being seen at a weekend rather than having to take time off work for a weekday appointment.

All members of staff were out to impress; attired in their smart new uniforms and wearing their old but genuine smiles they did their best to please – not always an easy task at times in the light of all these changes, but the good thing was that human nature does not change like buildings and our patients with their sense of humour remained the same. As we were soon reminded when Mr Jones arrived at the new surgery for his appointment and when he checked in at the reception he was informed that the doctor he had an appointment with was consulting upstairs. Because Mr Jones was not able to climb the stairs this meant he would have to use the lift in the waiting room for the first time.

He gingerly entered the lift which related a welcoming record-ed message as he stepped in. This took Mr Jones by surprise. He then had to take a step back as he startlingly came face to face with his own reflection in the large mirror that was fitted on the back wall of the lift. Then came many attempts to try and operate the lift, pressing the wrong buttons, an action that caused the doors to open and shut several times in full view of the patients in the downstairs waiting room. On a final attempt the doors of the lift opened to reveal a frustrated Mr Jones facing the mirror, asking his reflection, 'How do you get out of here?' All to the amusement of the onlooking audience of patients who had been kept entertained by Mr Jones and his lift adventure while they waited to see the doctor: and not one of them thought to get up and help him fathom it out.

Nevertheless Mr Jones was by no means the only patient who found it difficult to operate the lift. Mr Taylor, after several attempts of trying in vain to operate the same lift in the hope of reaching the first floor where his doctor was waiting to consult with him, found the doors of the lift opened yet again to the same familiar faces in the full waiting room downstairs staring back at him.

Seeing Mr Taylor's embarrassment Stella, the receptionist, left her busy desk (which was next to the lift) to help him out, by reaching into the lift where Mr Taylor stood and pressing the appropriate button to operate the lift. The doors closed once again only to open a few moments later on return to the ground floor and reveal at last an empty lift.

Stella, who was still waiting by the door of the lift, then bowed to the full waiting room and announced, 'And that's magic.' To which the full waiting room applauded as she took her second bow before returning to her desk.

After a few months of working in the new building it was decided by the partners that there had to be an official opening of the grand premises and a list was composed as to who should be invited to attend the event. The list contained names of people from the Shropshire Health Authority and the local community such as chemists, opticians, local traders as well as friends and colleagues from neighbouring practices along with members and friends of our own staff.

Dr Munro the founder of the Boweryhill Surgery who had now retired from his practice in Stovey, kindly agreed to travel from Scotland with his wife Dr Turnball to honour us by officially opening the new Boweryhill Surgery. The big night arrived after a busy day in which the staff once again had been occupied at every given moment in cleaning and tidying and making the final touches to rooms to help enhance the look in an effort to present the very best image to impress our visitors.

Once the last appointments of the day had left the premises the cleaners quickly spruced up the consulting rooms and helped arrange the wonderful display of food delivered for the buffet later. When the guests arrived they were greeted with a welcoming glass of refreshment as they gathered in the main reception area, where the members of staff did their best to mingle and chat, answering any questions raised by the visitors, while they waited for the introduction to the practice and the official speech from Dr Munro.

Once Dr Munro had unveiled the new brass plaque mounted in the waiting room and delivered his amusing speech, the guests were invited to feel free to browse around the surgery, and eventually to make their way upstairs to enjoy the refreshments laid out for them in the boardroom. Here the party enjoyed exchanging views and opinions on what they had seen, while the staff waited on providing tasty nibbles and keeping the visitors' glasses topped up, which added to a lively, extended evening.

Now that the official opening was well and truly over, the following morning it was back to work as normal with the reality of too many patients and not enough appointments to accommodate the demand. The new building had plenty of floor space and the female medical staff occupied the consulting room on the ground floor: I was in Room 1 next to the lift and opposite the reception room door: Val, a second practice nurse, had Room 4: the two rooms between us, 2 and 3 housed Dr Amber and Dr Breeze: on the opposite side of the corridor Heidi, the third practice nurse, had her room; and the healthcare assistants each had a room. The treatment room where certain nursing procedures such as dressings, ear syringing and ECGs were carried out, was situated at the end of the long corridor; this meant that at least the nurses got a fair amount of daily exercise running back and forward between patients: then added to this was the running up and down from the ground floor to the consulting rooms upstairs where Dr Cummingham, Dr Killjoy, and Dr Butter-Field, the male doctors, had their rooms next to a second waiting room. Along the corridor from the doctors were the offices of the clerical staff, and the practice manager's room, opposite the boardroom and large staff room.

On the right-hand side of the waiting room were the offices of the district nurses and health visitor and their clinic room, opposite the minor surgery room. At each end of the corridor was a staircase. Although the layout of the new premises was ideal for keeping the staff physically fit there was one who felt he was not getting enough daily workouts and came in one day wearing a pedometer. Dr Killjoy spent a lot of his working hours sitting in his consulting room treating his patients, and the rest of the time on his computer which meant that he most likely did need the exercise. So in an effort to clock up some miles on his monitor he would walk across the road to the local baker at lunchtime to collect his sandwiches, a gesture that made him feel fitter.

Shortly after the official opening the staff were back on form, thinking of ways to enjoy the time at work. Before long it was suggested that we could have a 'Guess Who the Baby Is' event. Each practice member was asked if they would bring in a photograph of themselves as a baby and give it to the clerk who displayed the funny faces on the noticeboard in the staff room; the staff had fun during the coffee break guessing who the babies were, and the monies raised went to a charity.

In reality the nurses' workload in the new surgery had increased, probably helped by the fact that the new building, which was nearer the centre of Bendigo and the shops, made it easier for the patients to drop in while passing. So it was not surprising that any free appointments were soon used up. After checking my appointment list Shirley the medical secretary informed me one morning that her nephew had made an appointment to see me later that day, then went on to say, 'Oh, by the way, he is very nervous because he is not used to coming to the surgery.'

Shirley, who is Irish, enjoys a laugh (like myself) and asked me to play a joke on her nephew if I was given the opportunity. 'If you could tease him while he is here you would put him at ease,' she winked.

Later that afternoon the unsuspecting nephew arrived for his consultation. He was a tall teenager, quiet in nature, and true to the information Shirley had given he was nervous. He presented with a minor ailment which I treated without too much concern, but then just before he was about to leave he plucked up the courage to ask, 'Would you check if my tummy is OK?'

I dutifully examined the young man's abdomen and now that he had provided me with the opportunity I asked him, 'Would you like to have your appendix out?' He looked at me in amazement. 'Would you like me to carry out the operation here and now?' Before I gave him the chance to answer I continued, 'Or would you like to be referred to the hospital?'

'Could you do it now?' he sheepishly asked.

Containing the grin that I felt creeping across my face I asked, 'Would you please lie on the examination couch?' pointing him in the direction of the couch. 'I'll collect my instruments from the steriliser.'

Without a moment's hesitation I left the room and returned fully masked and gowned carrying the largest, shiniest pair of forceps I could find. When I entered the room I found the young man trustingly lying back on the couch waiting for the unknown to happen. His eyes were the size of saucers as he caught sight of the forceps. It was all too much, I could not contain my laughter any longer, then to top it all at that precise moment his Aunt Shirley entered the room and we both collapsed in a heap of giggles as I explained to him that Shirley had put me up to the prank.

After a few seconds he relaxed as his Aunt Shirley confessed to being the culprit. Once I had contained myself I reassured him that he had no more wrong with him than a little muscle ache sustained from playing sport. His nervousness seemed to disappear as he replied, 'Aunt Shirley told me you were crazy but I did not know how crazy until now.'

Events like these helped to brighten up everyone's day as long as there was no harm done, and on the whole the patients enjoyed a bit of fun – it helped them relate to us better and certainly lessened their fears once they realised the medical staff were like themselves, human, and usually they would keep their follow-up appointments if they felt you were approachable. Although that young man never did come back, at least not to see me.

Nevertheless there were always a number of patients who were glad to see me, in or out of surgery: they did not mind as long as they could get an answer to anything that might be troubling them at that precise moment. I had just come out of the bank in Bendigo when I met Michelle, a patient I had treated on several occasions in the past, greeting me with affection. Michelle grasped the opportunity to ask me advice about her blood pressure: she was being treated for hypertension and was reluctant to take her medication in case she suffered from any side-effects, and because she did not have any headaches and felt OK she could not see the need to comply.

When Michelle spoke to me she was still annoyed at the doctor who at her last visit to the surgery had asked her on consultation if she had a life insurance policy.

'Yes,' was her surprised reply.

'Well, it won't cover you if you are not taking your pills,' he had warned.

'He was trying to blackmail me,' she told me.

This encounter with the doctor had made her ask my advice about flying and how it might affect her blood pressure.

'You see I had a terrible pain in my chest at the New Year,' she went on. 'And I asked my husband to take me to the hospital.'

'Oh you are OK,' he said, reluctant to get the car out. 'You are the wrong colour for a heart attack,' he tried to convince her.

'But you are only purple when you are dead,' she said.

With this last remark I started laughing and she could do no more than join in as she realised how funny it sounded.

'He never takes me seriously. I could have been dying,' she ended.

It was obviously a regular occurrence as far as her husband was concerned.

One busy Saturday morning in Morrisons supermarket in Minton I was silently going about my business filling my shopping trolley from my long list of items need to fill up our rather bare pantry at home, when I was distracted by someone slapping me on the shoulder.

'Hello Lynn, I am glad I have bumped into you,' said Mandy, a patient.

'Sarah, take off your shoe and show Lynn your verruca,' she ordered her daughter standing by.

'No, I can't look at it here,' I insisted.

'I am sure the management don't want verrucas exposed next to their freezers,' I stated.

'Oh, perhaps not,' blushed Mandy. 'I'll bring her to see you at the surgery,' she said moving away.

I never minded helping patients out where ever it might be but I had to draw the line sometimes and in the middle of food shopping was such a time.

Out of hours treatment was not all that frequent and never a problem as long as I had the necessary dressings at hand. On the odd occasion our doorbell would ring and I would open the door to a patient or neighbour who was unfortunate enough to have an accident, usually minor, such as a sprained wrist or cut that I was able to help out with.

However there was inevitably always the odd exception, as was the case one evening when Keith and I had just settled down to watch a film after dinner when the back doorbell went. I was more than surprised to open the door to a fairly fit male patient holding a tube of ointment in his hand.

'Lynn, I wonder if you could do me a favour?' he asked.

'What might that be?' was my puzzled reply

'Would you put this ointment the doctor gave me on my leg?'

Knowing he had travelled a reasonable distance and it was now dark outside, I could not turn him away. 'Come in. I will take you into the sitting room as my husband is in the lounge watching TV.'

At the speed of lightning I quickly applied the ointment to his leg and confirmed that it was certainly something he could do himself in future.

'Thanks very much, Lynn, I knew you would put it on correctly,' he casually replied.

'Yes, but I am sure your wife could too,' I said, as I closed the door and went back to my film.

30

Haste Ye Back!

During the weeks leading up to my retirement many of my appointments were taken up with patients that I had been treating and had known for years coming in to say their farewells to me.

It was a Monday afternoon when in came Angela, a lovely Irish lady who I had shared many a entertaining appointment within the past as we chatted about Ireland, during which time I had learnt about her family in her homeland and shared her grief when she lost a family member.

This was Angela's last visit to me and as soon as she entered my room she said, 'Lynn, I am upset that you're going.'

Being touched by her sadness I was about to reassure her when she continued, 'But before you go could you squeeze the blackhead on my back?'

Having my bubble burst I was soon brought back down to earth, although I should have been prepared, after all this was nothing new; in the past I had examined her back many times in search of spots or pimples that were not welcome and that her husband just could not bring himself to touch. So without hesitation and in a last attempt to please this nice lady for the last time, I found the offending blackhead and squeezed it. When Angela said her goodbyes and departed she did so leaving me knowing that she left me with something; unfortunately it was the unwanted blackhead which had discharged all over my face.

I had more or less forgotten about my uncomfortable experience with Angela the afternoon before when Roy arrived mid-morning on Tuesday to be seen. For the last few years I had been treating him on a regular basis every six weeks, and once again his six-week appointment had come around, and as usual Roy's remarkable cheerful attitude to life showed as he entered the room.

'Sorry you're going, Lynn. I have brought you a card,' he said.

He handed me an envelope which I opened, saying, 'That's lovely, thank you Roy.'

He looked at me as I read the card before he said, 'I was going to buy you something but I didn't.'

I thought, this is the type of thing that makes my day, and trying to hide my smile I replied, 'That's OK, Roy, the card is lovely.'

Then there were the patients who surprised me by very kindly presenting me with gifts. Jackie was one who attended for an appointment one afternoon to say her farewell.

'I have brought you a little gift, Lynn,' she said, handing me a fancy package.

'Oh, that is very kind of you,' I said as I accepted it, embarrassed.

Opening it I revealed a lovely necklace. Quite overcome I said it was too much.

'No, not at all. I have a lot to thank you for,' she insisted.

Jackie had attended the Help to Quit Clinic and had successfully given up smoking after many years. 'Every time I think I want a cigarette I think of Lynn Smart and what she would say,' she laughed. 'And that is enough to help me dismiss the idea of giving in to smoking ever again.'

I must admit, hearing that I had made an impression on Jackie who had now stopped smoking for well over a year, meant a lot to me.

Of all of the many gifts I was privileged to receive, one that had to be very special was a small teapot with a hand-knitted tea cosy covering it, given to me with love by an elderly couple who I had treated over many years. What made this present extra special was the knowledge that the tea cosy had been knitted to perfection by this dear lady who was blind.

These were the patients, like many others, who I would not forget. Another was Mary, whom I had known since I had started at the practice and over the years had visited me regularly. We enjoyed personal banter each time we met and although some would say Mary was one of life's rough diamonds, she certainly was a character and over the years we had shared many a joke; but she always took me seriously when it came to complying to her treatment.

The last visit Mary made to me was during my last week when she arrived for her appointment accompanied by her son. When they entered the room I felt a lump in my throat as Mary stood there in her best outfit, all polished up, holding a large bouquet of flowers while her son stood dressed in his best suit holding a large present that contained a cut glass vase to put the flowers in. Although the gifts were lovely, the thing that touched me most was the effort Mary had gone to say her goodbyes. Before she left we talked about the day Mary had just had her bath and put on her 'sponge dressing gown' as she called it. Then just as she sat on the edge of her bed and took off her dressing gown to get dressed, the phone rang. Mary, leaning forward, picked up the receiver. Suddenly her dog, a Jack Russell, jumped on her bare back and tried to bite the mole that seemed to flinch on Mary's back caused by the movement of her arms.

Later that same afternoon Hilary arrived to have her blood pressure checked, and after removing her coat, cardigan and two jumpers to reveal her arm, she asked, 'Oh, by the way, can you do anything about this mole on my head?'

'No,' I said, 'but I know a dog that can.'

Wednesday morning, and as I called on the intercom for my next patient Amy knocked on my door: she had arrived for her routine blood pressure check and wearing her usual smile said, 'I am upset, Lynn. I bought you a card, but I said to my husband I cannot give her this.'

'Why?' Her husband had asked.

'Because it is for a man. The teddy bear in front of the card is wearing a tie,' said Amy.

Seeing how disappointed she looked I reassured her, 'Never mind, Amy, it does not matter.'

She looked at me in surprise before saying, 'No! Lynn it is OK, we rushed out and got you another one.' Amy then handed me a large pink envelope.

Another large pink envelope sent to me was from one dear old lady patient named Sarah whom I had seen on several occasions in the past to check her blood pressure. She often chatted to me during her appointment about the birds that she spent hours watching in her garden: this was when she would describe the birds' habits and educate me as to the different types of feathered friends that were regular visitors in her area.

In my final week at work Sarah sent me a retirement card in which she enclosed a two-paged letter telling me what her pet budgie could say. This long letter puzzled me at first glance until I thought about it and finally came up with the conclusion that perhaps this was her only way of saying her last farewell, by letting her budgie say cheerio: although I did wonder who was crazy, the patient or me.

It was a sunny morning as I made my way to the surgery. Walking under the flyover bridge that is the South Route and along the ring road towards the impressive building, I could not believe this was to be my last working day there; how the years had flown – was I really going to be 60 in a few weeks' time? I would be joining the ranks of the pensioners. The thought did not bother me, I was really looking forward to retirement and all the free time I hoped to enjoy with Keith who was already retired and had been for more than two years now. However, I did wonder after working full-time and having dealt with as many as 37-plus appointments every day, how I would fill my free time. I knew I would miss the people who I had attended to over the past 36 years and the fun we had shared, but I was not intending to leave Bendigo so I would doubtless see them out and about. That is, if Keith and I were not away on our travels, which we hoped to do now that the fulfilment of our dreams and plans was just on the horizon.

As I approached the surgery I suddenly felt a little nervous and wondered what the day might have in store for me. Nevertheless I did not have to wonder long because as I entered the practice I was greeted with a display of fancy decorations, balloons, streamers, numerous banners, and posters with humorous Scottish slogans plastered on doors and walls around the surgery for all to see. I opened the door of my consulting room to find it full of dolls, prams, baby baths and decor that related back to my time as a midwife. Once I had read the many posters displayed around the room I composed myself and switched on the computer to look at the day's appointments: not that I expected many because the day before I had blanked off my appointment screen, feeling that I might not be able to cope emotionally with saying my good-byes, and my nursing colleagues had reassured me they were only too willing to deal with the necessary appointments requested on my last day.

As my screen opened up it revealed a list of free appointments, apart from the first 8.30 slot that showed Mr Johnson booked and waiting. I called him in and when he entered he sat down.

'I have a nice job for you on your last day,' he grinned.

'And what might that be?' I smiled back.

'This,' he said. Then taking off his jacket and lifting his shirt he revealed a large pus-filled abscess sitting on his left shoulder.

'Let's get you down to the treatment room where I can lance it,' I replied.

Once I had released the foul-smelling copious quantity of green pus and applied a dressing I instructed Mr Johnson to make a follow-up appointment to have a further dressing. Feeling he had done me a favour he replied, 'You will be glad you have done something useful on your last day, enjoy your retirement.'

'Yes I am sure I will,' were my parting words to him.

On returning to my room I was met by a jolly bunch of staff

members who had temporarily abandoned their posts and their uniforms to wear white T-shirts with a picture of my face plastered across their chests. If that alone was not enough to put people off, they carted me away and having dished out similar actions to them in the past, I now had to pay the price and receive a bit back by allowing my workmates to dressed me up in rolls of material and decorate me with plumes of feathers and anything else that was at hand before completing the picture by putting a pair of tartan granny slippers on my feet, then parading me through the waiting rooms on view to the poor patients who were hoping to get treated sometime that day.

The hours that followed were a constant flow of ongoing tricks and antics carried out by staff and colleagues alike at every given moment between what was supposed to be a normal working day. At around eleven a few of the girls collected me from my room where I was taken upstairs to the full staff room where two policemen stepped forward to meet me.

'Oh no, you're not going to take your clothes off?' I gasped, thinking they were some sort of strippergram.

'No we are real policemen,' they both said, shocked. 'We have come to remove you from these premises,' said the taller of the two.

And to my amazement they handcuffed me, before each of them put a hand on my shoulders to guide me through the upstairs waiting room, down the stairs through the ground floor waiting room and outside to the car park, where they intended to place me in the back seat of their police car. But before they could get me into the car I managed to put my handcuffed wrists over one policeman's head and before he had a chance to escape I pulled him down and gave him a kiss; now he was blushing and protesting, saying, 'I am on duty and the public are watching.'

'Whose fault is that?' I laughed, looking around to a sea of faces that had gathered to watch what was happening.

The officers quickly escorted me back to the staff room and

released me from the handcuffs, Now joined by all the practice staff including those who were booked on leave and the cleaners who were not due to start work until the evening, we all tucked into the buffet lunch the surgery had provided.

Leaving the surgery a few hours later, when Keith called to drive me home, was not too emotional. After having shared a great deal of laughter throughout the day my mood was one of happiness, and I knew I would be meeting up with everyone again that evening at the farewell dinner which had been arranged. The minor problem I had in leaving the building was trying to carry the mountain of flowers that had been delivered to my room from thankful patients, along with gifts I had received from both friends and patients throughout the day. These items together with the personal belongings that had occupied my room for so long soon filled the car, leaving me to wave good bye and head for home.

We had only been home for a few moments when a lorry pulled up outside the house and Jeff, one of the patients, dismounted from his cab and carrying a lovely arrangement of flowers came to the front door.

'I just missed you at the surgery, Lynn, and would like to give you these.'

'Thank you, Jeff, make sure you look after yourself.'

Jeff was always a regular appointment every Christmas who called just to bring a musical Christmas card, and the last Christmas present he had given me was a musical Santa that wiggled his hips as he played. I used it as a source of amusement which also acted as a distraction for any child who attended for treatment. No doubt my replacement would be certain to receive a Christmas visit from Jeff, who was so thoughtful and just loved giving out the latest design in musical Christmas cards.

The afternoon soon flew past and in what seemed like no time Keith and I were getting ready to meet everyone for the evening celebrations. It was nice of the partners to allow me to invite some of my family to the meal, especially since they employed a large number of staff and the chosen venue was known to be expensive. Although Flo had tried to persuade me to invite my brothers to travel from Scotland, it was not practical to expect them to drop their commitments in order to make the long journey just for one night, therefore apart from Keith I had only asked Margaret and Helen, my two sisters, accompanied by their husbands to come and we had arranged to meet at the hotel. The venue was convenient for them especially Helen and Jack who lived in the same area. When we arrived Helen and Jack were already there and told me they had just been barred from entering the banqueting hall by the hotelier who thought they were gatecrashing.

'But I am the sister of the main guest,' Helen had protested.

'Well wait in the bar, because no one can enter the room until she does,' said the hotelier

I knew from the start that this was going to turn out to be a fun night: who needs hired entertainment when you have family that will always oblige? The fact that it is a member of the Dickie family means fun can be guaranteed. In this instance there were three Dickie sisters prepared to make it a night to remember.

The Castle Bank Hotel, within the walls of which lies local historic interest, proved to be an excellent choice of venue, with ample room to accommodate the many guests invited in the grand banqueting hall with its huge oval table enhanced by the splendid dressings upon it, the image of which was reflected on the mirrored wall at the far end of the room. Surrounding this great table were high-backed, carved oak chairs, one of which had been covered with tartan drapes and was in centre position of the table reserved for me.

When all the guests had arrived and had time to collect a drink of their choice from the bar, we were beckoned to take a seat at the dining table. Everyone could sit where they liked other than myself who was asked to 'take my throne,' which I dutifully did with Helen on the right of me and Shirley on the left, making the combination of Scottish and Irish a noisy section of the table. I did feel honoured that I should be treated so well, and was touched by the effort everyone had put in to ensure that the night was a success. One wall of the room was covered in photographs of past and present members of staff that had been taken down through the years since I had started at the surgery. After the meal a member of the staff read out a poem:

An Ode to Lynn

Lynn our nurse at Boweryhill Street
Is retiring today to put up her feet
She loves a laugh and is always loud
And she acted the fool to many a crowd

She's seen so many come and go
Drs Blessington, Samuels, Cummingham, and Mo
Dr Turnball and Dr Munro are a few you knew
And then there was Bert a character too

Dr Gardener was a very quiet man
And Dr Samuels was your biggest fan
Dr Goode who lived like a farmer
She even bred chickens, dogs and the odd llama

Dr Daffin was a Jack-the-lad
He was always naughty and sometimes bad
Dr Moil who was loved so much
And Dr Killjoy who thinks he's butch

Dr Jeffs who caused quiet a stir
He came and went – it was all a blur
Dr Burton came from overseas
And our gorgeous broken-armed Dr Breeze

Dr Butter-Field he's one of a kind
He's leaving soon, happiness we hope he'll find
Dr Amber was our last recruit
She loves a laugh and finds us all a hoot

Dr Cummingham, how could we forget?
No replacement as of yet

Remember the time you did *This is Your Life*
And Dr Cummingham dressed as an old fishwife
And the time poor Flo broke her wrists
A joke you thought and gave them a twist

A baby was born into your tender hands
It was rather quick and surely unplanned
They called him Jamie and not after you
Then again you didn't expect them to

Your time line shows you at many a do
With members of the Boweryhill Crew
It's time to hang up your nurse's gear
And bid you farewell with an almighty cheer

Goodbye, Farewell and Au Revoir
We know you'll never be very far
And now it's really time to go
And we will all miss you so

Thank you Lynn, for all you've done
Enjoy your time and have lots of fun.

   She presented this to me along with a photo album that contained an individual picture of each member of the practice together with the farewell message they had written: this I found very moving and decided to wait until I was home before looking all the way through it.

Dr Cummingham gave a very nice speech where he recalled some of the fun events we had shared in the practice in the past, and some of the unpredictable things I had done. He then went on to say, 'The most recent was one morning while I was consulting with a couple, the husband of which had just been diagnosed as having an acute illness and I was just pondering how to comfort them, when I was interrupted by Lynn knocking on the door and coming in to have a prescription signed for a patient waiting in her room. While I was signing the request, Lynn took one look at the glum faces of my patients sitting there before asking, "What is this?" And without hesitation bent her knees and took up the position of sitting, stuck out her right arm, turned left by shuffling around the room in a circle, before stopping in front of us. "An Irish bus driver turning right," she answered. Then taking the prescription she departed, totally unaware of the circumstances, leaving us in the room smiling but speechless.'

This was the first time Dr Cummingham had told me about the circumstances of that couple, probably to spare my feelings, because the last thing I had intended to do was cause them any more grief. In this instance, as far as I was concerned, ignorance was bliss. The evening ended with a Scottish piper entering the room playing a selection of famous tunes on his familiar bagpipes: the sight of this final surprise instinctively resulted in we three Dickie sisters getting up and dancing a Highland Fling to the music while the rest of the guests looked on, managing to tolerate the din by having yet another glass of wine. Not that the alcohol dulled their hearing, but it did have an effect on their senses helping them endure what had to be the icing on the cake as far as I was concerned to a lovely evening.

It was an evening that all too quickly came to an end, and no matter how hard I tried to compose myself, the farewells brought on the tears as each individual guest gave me a parting hug and asked me to keep in touch. I cannot say they were tears of sadness, but more of delight as I was eager to find out what retirement had in store for me and if there really was life after Boweryhill Surgery.

I did not have to wait long to find out because after a few weeks into retirement I could fully understand all those patients in the past that had told me: 'Once you retire there are never enough hours in the day – you'll wonder how you ever had time to go to work.'

Then there was the odd exception like the lady who said, 'If you ever get bored, you can always work in a charity shop for a few days a week. I do.'

Sure enough I could now relate to them, as my now 'free days' were crammed with places to go and people to visit. At last there is no more time watching and the pleasure of being able to take off and travel without worrying about using up all your annual leave is great. So travel we did, spending weeks at a time visiting Ireland and now with the budget flights available on the Internet (I have always been one for a bargain) there have been many opportunities to travel across the Continent.

But the most delightful thing about meeting different people whatever their nationality is that you can always find their sense of humour is normally the same the world over, as was the case when I was travelling in Slovenia and an old German woman who did not speak a word of English, asked me to feel the patch on her buttock that her doctor had given her to help cure the pain in her right shoulder. I can honestly say yes there is life after Boweryhill practice.

'Lynn, what are you going to do now that you've retired?'

'Oh, I would like to write a book.'

'That sounds like a good idea. What will the book be about?'

'About the people I have had the pleasure of treating over the years.'

'Can I be in the book?'

'Well, there will be a lot to tell.'

'Let me know when the book is out.'

'If it ever gets finished,' was my parting word.